CONTENTS

 Pedigree Books Ltd, Beech Hill House, Walnut Gardens, Exeter, Devon EX4 4DH
www.pedigreebooks.com I books@pedigreegroup.co.uk I Published 2009.

£7.99

SO YOU THINK YOU KNOW SINNOH

Take a look at the Island of Sinnoh. Stunning, isn't it? Its crystal blue lakes, warm seas, dense forests and mountain ridges are simply teeming with Pokémon. Ash is getting to meet more and more species as he continues his travels through this exciting and diverse region.

For all its beauty Sinnoh is not without challenges, but luckily Ash isn't alone. His good friends Dawn and Brock are by his side and loyal Pikachu is always on his shoulder. The trio are making many new friends and crossing paths with old adversaries. They're also taking on some great rivals such as Angie who they come across at the Pokémon Summer Camp. From Gym Battles to Contests the excitement never ends.

KEY

1. Solaceon Town
2. Eterna City
3. Eterna Forest
4. Veilstone City
5. Lake Valor
6. Newmoon Island
7. Mount Coronet
8. Cycling Road & Wayward Cave
9. Pastoria City
10. Twinleaf Town

HEROES' WELCOME

ASH

If you don't know the name Ash Ketchum, then where have you been? The young trainer is blazing a trail through the world of Pokémon, demonstrating skill and courage far beyond his years. Now he's built up an awesome reputation as a Pokémon Trainer.

Having left his home in Pallet Town at the age of ten, Ash began the long journey towards becoming a Pokémon Master. He has already travelled through the regions of Kanto, Johto and Hoenn – now he finds himself in the mountainous region of Sinnoh. Ash's success is largely down to his strong character. His unshakeable confidence in his own ability means he can come across as arrogant and big-headed at first, but eventually his enthusiasm and passion for all things Pokémon win over even his toughest rivals and critics.

HEROES' WELCOME
PIKACHU

Where Ash goes, Pikachu follows. Or should that be rides…! Unlike most Pokémon, feisty Pikachu flatly refuses the usual Poké Ball method of transport. Instead the sparky Electric Pokémon prefers to perch on Ash's shoulder.

Unconventional the partnership may be, but the pair are the best of friends. The fact that Ash and Pikachu are never apart means that they have formed an unshakeable bond that goes far beyond the traditional Pokémon-human relationship. This wasn't always the case however. At first there was a personality clash between the headstrong Trainer and his wilful Pokémon. It took some time for the duo to appreciate each other's good qualities! Now Ash loves Pikachu's strength and loyalty, while Pikachu adores his master's bravery and compassion. With Brock and Dawn along for the ride, Ash and Pikachu can overcome any obstacle or challenge that their journey may hold.

HEROES' WELCOME
BROCK

Brock and Ash go way back. The friends met when Ash battled at Pewter City Gym, discovering that its Leader was a young man on his own wavelength, but with maturity and wisdom to boot. Becoming a Gym Leader was never Brock's calling. For years he held the fort for his father, but he'd always dreamt of becoming a top Breeder. Joining Ash on his quest has allowed him to finally follow his heart.

Brock is thoughtful, creative and always on hand with tips or advice on how to handle a new Pokémon or sticky situation. He loves to cook and always has some homemade poffins or special re-energising food to hand when bonding with wild Pokémon. His one weakness is girls. Luckily whenever he goes gooey, Croagunk, his traveling companion of choice in Sinnoh, zaps some sense into him with its toxic jab.

HEROES' WELCOME
DAWN

Ash and Brock love having Dawn around. Bursting with smiles and wisecracks, she is a great travelling companion. The young girl has another thing in common with her friends however – talent. Dawn has proved herself to be a highly skilled Pokémon Co-ordinator, just like her mother Johanna.

As a Co-ordinator, Dawn enters her Pokémon in Contests where they are judged on the beauty of their moves rather than their ability to fell an opponent. Having said that, she isn't averse to a battle! Her journey through Sinnoh is offering her ample opportunity to show that she's a person of substance and skill, not just a girl with great fashion sense.

HEROES' WELCOME
TEAM ROCKET

Jessie, James and Meowth are Team Rocket, a hapless outfit whose main aim is to create chaos wherever they land. They rap and rhyme to pass the time and live by the motto 'a rose by any other name would smell as sweet, when everything's worse our work is complete'. Luckily for our heroes, they're pretty clueless and so usually end up causing more trouble for themselves than they do for anyone else.

Every troop of monkeys needs an organ grinder, and Team Rocket's is the elusive and evil Giovanni. He wants Jessie, James and Meowth to capture Ash's Pikachu because of its unique powers. They'll do anything to impress their master by achieving this goal, no matter what it takes. As time goes by their frustration is growing and their schemes are becoming ever more desperate and daft. Whether they're disguising themselves in homemade costumes or luring Pokémon into traps, one thing's for sure – Team Rocket don't give up easily.

EVOLVED AND IMPROVED

Check out these pictures of Gabite and its even more fearsome evolved form Garchomp. Can you pinpoint and describe eight ways in which Garchomp is different from its prior evolution? You'll need to use all your powers of observation...

GABITE

GARCHOMP

Garchomp has

1. _____

2. _____

3. _____

4. _____

5. _____

6. _____

7. _____

8. _____

For two extra points, can you think of something that differentiates the Pokémon that isn't actually visible?

9. _____

10. _____

Check the answers at the back of the book and then award yourself a mark out of ten!

Score _____

ABOMASNOW

TYPE: GRASS-ICE
ABILITY: SNOW WARNING
HEIGHT: 2.2m
WEIGHT: 135.5kg

What we humans refer to as the mythical 'Abominable Snowman' or 'Yeti' looks a bit like this Grass-Ice type Pokémon. Abomasnow whips up blizzards in mountains to ensure they stay buried in snow.

BRONZONG

TYPE: STEEL-PSYCHIC
ABILITY: LEVITATE-HEATPROOF
HEIGHT: 1.3m
WEIGHT: 187.0kg

This curious metallic Pokémon hit the headlines when it was dug up from a construction site. It was believed to have lain there for around 2,000 years.

BRONZOR

TYPE: STEEL-PSYCHIC
ABILITY: LEVITATE-HEATPROOF
HEIGHT: 0.5m
WEIGHT: 60.5kg

It is rumoured that implements shaped like Bronzor were found in ancient tombs. It is not known if this is the truth or a myth. Bronzor evolves into Bronzong.

BUIZEL

TYPE: WATER
ABILITY: SWIFT SWIM
HEIGHT: 0.7m
WEIGHT: 29.5kg

Buizel swims by rotating its two tails like a screw. It also boasts a collar-like flotation sac which inflates on water but collapses when it needs to dive below the surface.

CHANSEY

TYPE: NORMAL
ABILITY: NATURAL CURE-SERENE GRACE
HEIGHT: 1.1m
WEIGHT: 34.6kg

Believed to deliver happiness, this Pokémon is very caring. Chansey often works with Nurse Joy. It shares its eggs with the sick and injured. This Pokémon evolves into Blissey.

CRESSELIA

TYPE: PSYCHIC
ABILITY: LEVITATE
HEIGHT: 1.5m
WEIGHT: 85.6kg

Shiny particles are released from Cresselia's wings like a veil. This Psychic Pokémon has no evolutions at all. It is said to represent the crescent moon.

CROAGUNK

TYPE: POISON-FIGHTING

ABILITY: ANTICIPATION-DRY SKIN

HEIGHT: 0.7m

WEIGHT: 23.0kg

Toxicroak's first evolution has poison sacs embedded in its cheeks. When the sacs inflate, Croagunk emits an intimidating blubbering sound that helps it to catch foes off-guard.

DRIFBLIM

TYPE: GHOST-FLYING

ABILITY: AFTERMATH-UNBURDEN

HEIGHT: 1.2m

WEIGHT: 15.0kg

This nocturnal Pokémon is drowsy by day, but flies off in groups in the evenings. Its destination remains unknown to even the most expert Breeders.

DRIFLOON

TYPE: GHOST-FLYING

ABILITY: AFTERMATH-UNBURDEN

HEIGHT: 1.2m

WEIGHT: 1.2kg

This Pokémon is created from the spirits of both Pokémon and humans. Drifloon seeks out damp, humid climates before evolving into the wafting form of Drifblim.

DUSKNOIR

TYPE: GHOST

ABILITY: PRESSURE

HEIGHT: 2.2m

WEIGHT: 106.6kg

The antenna on Dusknoir's head captures radio waves from the world of spirits. These frequencies often prompt the Pokémon to take people there. It has a tapered tail instead of feet.

DUSKULL

TYPE: GHOST

ABILITY: LEVITATE

HEIGHT: 0.8m

WEIGHT: 15.0kg

This spooky Pokémon evolves into Dusclops and then finally Dusknoir. It doggedly pursues its prey all night, but will relent at sunrise. An eerie red light glows from behind its skull.

FINNEON

TYPE: WATER

ABILITY: SWIFT STORM-STORM DRAIN

HEIGHT: 0.4m

WEIGHT: 7.0kg

After lengthy exposure to sunlight, the patterns on this Pokémon's tail fins glow in the dark. Its butterfly-shaped tail is a thing of exceptional beauty. Finneon evolves into Lumineon.

FLOATZEL

TYPE: WATER

ABILITY: SWIFT SWIM

HEIGHT: 1.1m

WEIGHT: 33.5kg

Evolved from Buizel, Floatzel uses its highly evolved flotation sac to assist in the rescue of drowning people. This Pokémon is an extremely useful Water-type to have around!

FROSLASS

TYPE: ICE-GHOST

ABILITY: SNOW CLOAK

HEIGHT: 1.3m

WEIGHT: 26.6kg

One of Snorant's two evolutions, Froslass freezes foes with an icy breath of over -50º degrees C. What seems to be its silvery body is actually a hollow cavity.

GABITE

TYPE: DRAGON-GROUND

ABILITY: SAND VEIL

HEIGHT: 1.4m

WEIGHT: 56.0kg

Gabite is the middle evolution between Gible and Garchomp. This Pokémon is worth looking out for – there is a long-held belief that medicine made from Gabite's scales will heal even incurable illnesses.

GALLADE

TYPE: PYSCHIC-FIGHTING

ABILITY: STEADFAST

HEIGHT: 1.6m

WEIGHT: 52.0kg

A master of courtesy and swordsmanship, Gallade fights using extending swords attached to its elbows. The Pokémon is one of Kirlia's two evolutions – the other is Gardevoir.

GARCHOMP

TYPE: DRAGON-GROUND

ABILITY: SAND VEIL

HEIGHT: 1.9m

WEIGHT: 95kg

Evolved from Gible and Gabite, this Pokémon uses its huge wingspan to fly at sonic speed. When in flight, Gabite is said to resemble a sleek jet plane.

GASTRODON

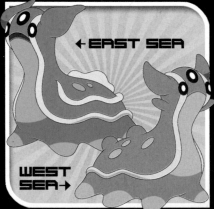

← EAST SEA

WEST SEA →

TYPE: WATER-GROUND

ABILITY: STICKY HOLD-STORM DRAIN

HEIGHT: 0.9m

WEIGHT: 29.9kg

This slug-like Pokémon evolves from Shellos. Its body has no bones whatsoever. If any part of Gastrodon gets torn off in combat, it will grow back again.

GIBLE

TYPE: DRAGON-GROUND

ABILITY: SAND VEIL

HEIGHT: 0.7m

WEIGHT: 20.5kg

This aggressive Dragon-Ground type Pokémon nests in small holes tucked in cave walls. Gible will wait hours for the right moment, pouncing on any prey that gets too close.

GLACEON

TYPE: ICE

ABILITY: SNOW CLOAK

HEIGHT: 0.8m

WEIGHT: 25.9kg

As a protective technique, Glaceon can completely freeze its fur so that its hairs stand up like sharp needles. This Ice type Pokémon is just one of Eevee's seven evolutions.

GLISCOR

TYPE: GROUND-FLYING

ABILITY: HYPER CUTTER-SAND VEIL

HEIGHT: 2.0m

WEIGHT: 42.5kg

Evolved from Gligar, Gliscor observes prey while hanging upside down from trees. At the right moment the bat-like Pokémon will swoop in to attack.

HIPPOPOTAS

TYPE: GROUND

ABILITY: SAND STREAM

HEIGHT: 0.8m

WEIGHT: 49.5kg

It lives in dry places because it hates to get wet. Instead of perspiration, this lumbering Pokémon sweats out grainy sand from its body. Hippopotas evolves into Hippowdon.

HIPPOWDON

TYPE: GROUND

ABILITY: SAND STREAM

HEIGHT: 2.0m

WEIGHT: 300.0kg

This mammoth beast's most awesome attack move involves blasting internally stored sand from ports in its flanks. In this sand blast Hippowdon is able to create a towering twister to blind its foe.

LEAFEON

TYPE: GRASS

ABILITY: LEAF GUARD

HEIGHT: 1.0m

WEIGHT: 25.5kg

Leafeon is another of Eevee's many evolutions. Just like a plant, the Grass Pokémon uses photosynthesis to process the air around it. As a result, Leafeon is always enveloped in a clear bubble.

CAMPING IT UP!

We're witnessing a mid-journey surprise for our Heroes! After being contacted by Professor Rowan, the gang is heading off to the Pokémon Summer Academy…

Ash, Dawn and Brock sprinted through the forest, kicking up a cloud of dust in their wake. "We're gonna be late guys, I know we are!" screamed Ash. "If you hadn't overslept we wouldn't have this problem," panted Dawn, angrily. "If you hadn't been tryin' to fix your dumb bedhead we also wouldn't have this problem!" grunted Ash. Dawn frowned. She hated to look dishevelled and always took a while to get ready in the morning. "Hurry up!" yelled a puffed-out Brock. The trio, accompanied as ever by Pikachu and Piplup, picked up their pace. They made it through the gates of a walled

complex just as a bell rang signalling the start of lessons. Ash breathed a sigh of relief. "Looks like we made it after all." "You're late!" boomed a voice across the square, as a grey-haired, white-coated man strode into view.

"Wow, it's Professor Rowan!" whispered Ash. "I welcome you to the Rowan Research Facility on Mount Coronet!" said the Professor proudly. "Or for all intents and purposes… your school!" Soon the grounds were filled with dozens of other eager young people. A teaching assistant directed them to a huge blackboard where their names had been listed in teams. "I'm on the Red team!" smiled Ash.

Dawn and Brock were delighted to find they too were in Red. "Looks like I'm on the Blue Team!" said a boy in glasses. The gang was shocked to see old rival Conway step forward. "Somehow I just knew you'd all be coming," he mocked.

"Don't forget meeeee!" trilled a familiar, sing-song voice. A girl with vibrant pink bunches, glasses and a whole lot of attitude stepped forward. "The name's Jessilinda and I'm on the Green Team!" she crowed smugly. "I'm also the school's resident Cutie Pie!" Lurking behind the students some other familiar faces were less than impressed. "Subtlety is a lost art with her…" moaned James. "Yeah," agreed Meowth. "Stickin' out like a sore thumb ain't exactly helpful when you're tryin' to swipe the school's Pokémon." The pair were disguised as maintenance engineers, and Jessie as a student – all part of Team Rocket's latest evil scheme.

Professor Rowan began to introduce the students. "Just as there are various kinds of Pokémon in various parts of our world, budding young trainers are no different! Destiny has brought you all together, so get to know one another and while you're at it have some fun!" Rowan's assistant then proposed a Battle as the way for the Pokémon to introduce themselves. "Each and everyone will use these Poké Balls!" said the Professor. "One per student!' "Come on!" grumbled Meowth. "That's the box of Poké Balls we were just poaching." "If we'd just been quicker on the thieving draw…" whined a frustrated James.

Meanwhile the students, completely unaware of the danger in their midst, were excited to learn that the Pokémon they'd be paired with was down to the luck of the draw. Ash eagerly stepped forward, but as he pulled out a Poké Ball from the box he realised someone else's hand was attached.
"Let go!" said the owner of the hand. "I got it first."
"I got it first!" Ash replied, glaring at the short-haired boy in the green top and combat trousers.

The struggle continued. Neither one of the boys would let go – both pulled furiously at the ball claiming it was theirs.
"There's nothing ruder than a guy who ignores Ladies First!" shrieked Ash's rival.
"You mean to tell me that you're a girl?" said Ash, jumping back and dropping the Poké Ball.
"Now you're really getting me mad!" said the girl. "The name's Angie – and I challenge you to a Battle!"

Ash readily agreed, introducing himself through clenched teeth and glaring at his equally fierce female opponent.
It was left to the Professor to break the stalemate.
"Good. That's the spirit!" he said. "But tomorrow's when the real battles start! The order of business today is to meet the Pokémon you chose!"
Angie wasted no time in calling hers out.
"Cool, a Monferno!" exclaimed Ash, consulting his Pokédex.

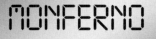

MONFERNO

THE PLAYFUL POKÉMON, AND THE EVOLVED FORM OF CHIMCHAR. MONFERNO LAUNCHES AERIAL ATTACKS OFF CEILINGS AND WALLS, AND ITS FIERY TAIL IS USED AS ONE OF ITS WEAPONS.

Angie politely introduced herself to her Monferno, but it just turned its head away.
"Looks like you rub Pokémon up the wrong way too," smirked Ash.

Still chuckling, he bent down to pick a Poké Ball for himself "OK, now it's my turn. Come on out!"
Quick as a flash, a Raichu appeared before him.
Ash was excited. "My name's Ash, I'm glad to meet you!"
But before he could approach the Raichu, the timid Pokémon burrowed itself into the ground, out of sight.
This time it was Angie's turn to laugh. "Ash, I think Raichu's scared of you!'
Ash bristled.
"Cool it!" he muttered. "We're gonna be friends real soon!"

Next it was Dawn's turn. Her Poké Ball revealed a Grimer. There were murmurs of disappointment from the crowd, and Dawn herself seemed worried by her Poké Partner, but seeing Grimer looking sad the kind Co-ordinator soon rallied.

"You're pretty cute you know," she told the Pokémon, only to be rewarded with a sticky embrace.
As she extracted herself from Grimer, Dawn noticed that Piplup was missing. The poor Pokémon was stuck in the folds of Grimer's goo!

"I'm next!" said Brock. His Poké Ball revealed a Magnemite, while Jessie got a Smoochum. Conway was paired with a Venonat. The square was soon filled with noise as the students called out and greeted their new Pokémon buddies.

The introductions weren't plain sailing for everyone though. Ash just couldn't coax his Raichu out of its hole. "Come on out please," he begged. "What's wrong with you?" Meanwhile Angie was hot-footing it round the grounds after her Monferno. The Pokémon was running away as fast as its feet would carry it. Suddenly Monferno ran into a Croconaw. Despite Croconaw's Trainer's panicked calls for them to chill out, the pair squared up to each other! Sensing tension, Pikachu jumped in to try to calm things. That caused Monferno to send out a storm of fiery amber that charred the electric Pokémon, who responded angrily with his Volt Tackle move.

"Don't treat Monferno like that!" yelled Angie, pulling out her own Poké Ball and summoning Shinx. "Use Spark on Pikachu," she commanded. Ash was quick to respond. "We'll show 'em Pikachu!" he cried. "Thunderbolt, let's go!" The two Pokémon clashed in a crackling ball of electricity. "Enough!" A shout echoed round the students. Professor Rowan was shaking with rage. "I never told you that you could use your own Pokémon in battle!" he roared, grabbing Angie and Ash by the scruff of their necks. The pair began to blame each other, but Rowan had no time for excuses. "This school is not the place for quarrelling!" he told them firmly. "It's for making new friends with people and Pokémon." The pair nodded sheepishly.

As the clock chimed, the Professor then explained that the first hour was over and that in tomorrow's Battle he would judge how well they'd all befriended their Pokémon. Points would be awarded accordingly.
"At the end of each section points are awarded by Professor Rowan," Angie told a confused Ash.
"On the final day the total number of points for each class team is added up to decide who's the big winner!" added Conway. Ash was psyched.
"The Red team's gonna win it all!" he exclaimed. 'Sure," said Angie. "Just as long as you don't hold us back!" The angry pair faced up each other again, but were interrupted by the assistant who had news of the next lesson. "Now as we move into our second hour, I want you all to work on getting closer to your new Pokémon," he said.

Inside the classroom the students worked at bonding with their Pokémon. Dawn tried to win Grimer over with a snack of Poffins. Angie was impressed.
"Wow you've got Poffins that are homemade?" she asked enviously.

At the next desk Brock offered his Magnemite some static electricity and gave it a brisk speed polish rub down. When he'd finished Magnemite's metal shone blindingly. "What a neat idea!" said Angie in awe. "His Magnemite looks great."

Unfortunately she didn't have quite the same handle on her Monferno. Once again the Pokémon was brawling with a fellow Red student's Croconaw. Angie hastily pulled Monferno away.

A sh faced his Raichu, perched on the desk in front of him. "Let's see what moves you can use…" he said, bringing out his Pokédex.

FOCUS PUNCH
DIG
THUNDERBOLT
DOUBLE TEAM

"Raichu, you can use Double Team too?" marvelled Ash. 'I can't wait for our battle to start!" Dawn's Pokédex was giving her the low-down on Grimer. If the explanation was distinctive, the moves were equally unique.

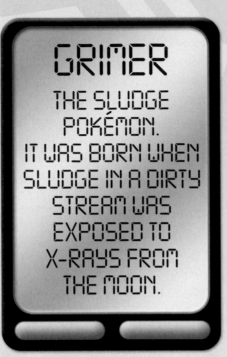

GRIMER
THE SLUDGE POKÉMON.
IT WAS BORN WHEN SLUDGE IN A DIRTY STREAM WAS EXPOSED TO X-RAYS FROM THE MOON.

POSION GAS
MUD SLAP
SLUDGE
GUNK SHOT

Dawn clapped her hands in glee. "No need to worry!" she beamed. "I just know you're going to shine Grimer." To make sure he did just that, Dawn began to rub oil into Grimer's body. She giggled as the Pokémon responded to her massage. Unfortunately she'd forgotten the downside of having a sludgy pal – suddenly her hand disappeared inside its head.

Ash too was attempting to spruce up his Pokémon.
"Now doesn't that feel great?" he asked Raichu, as he gently brushed its fur. Raichu finally seemed to be responding well until the brush got tangled. The Pokémon freaked out, sending Ash flying with electric shocks.

While the Red team were struggling at times, the others were doing well. Jessie was proclaiming her Smoochum even cuter than herself, while Conway was quietly discussing mathematical equations with his Venonat.

Refusing to give up on Grimer, Dawn stepped up her campaign to forge a relationship with it. "Now! I'm going to pose, and I want you to do what I do!" she said, striking first one stance and then another. Unbelievably Grimer mimicked her every move. With Piplup joining in they made a cool tableau. "Amazing!" laughed Dawn in delight. "You can pose any which way I can!"

"Now Monferno, we're going to practice a few of your moves!" said Angie, seeing the progress Dawn was making.

Again Monferno had other ideas. First it showered her with fire, and then it clambered up to the top of the blackboard and rained hot pellets down on Ash, Pikachu and Raichu. "Why me?" he seethed.

"Because you weren't paying attention, duh!" mocked Angie. Luckily their latest argument was broken up by the assistant's whistle.

The feuding pair landed themselves with a punishment.

"I still don't understand why I have to run laps!" moaned Ash.

"Cause you started it dummy!" panted Angie. Their rivalry spurred them on to try and outdo each other even in the courtyard. Soon they were puffed out and starving. Meanwhile the other students were eating lunch. Jessilinda (aka Jessie) was particularly enjoying her meal.

"For some strange reason I've forgotten what I'm doing here," she said. "Oh well who cares? Some more please!"

In the kitchen Meowth and James looked on proudly.

"She's eating the curry made from the fruits of our labour!" cried James.

"It's times like this that makes a gourmet chef as proud as punk!" agreed Meowth. Ash and Angie appeared at the door.

"Did you save us some?" asked Ash.

"Sorry no," said Dawn, then seeing their faces she added. "Just kidding!"

"Man, that's good!" said Ash, tucking in.

"For once we all agree!" laughed Dawn.

The rest of the afternoon was taken up with more tasks and studies, including an inter-group tug of war. Everybody worked hard, but Ash and Angie were so worn out they fell asleep during one class. At last it was time for bed. Ash, Dawn and Brock found themselves sharing a dormitory with Angie. Everyone got in their bunks but no-one could sleep. Angie suggested a game of cards.

"So Angie, you haven't started on your journey yet?' asked Ash, as they started playing.

"No, I've been working in a Pokémon daycare centre," she replied, "It's so busy. I hardly have a free moment."

"I can see it would be tough to find time for a journey," Brock said.

"But it's lots of fun and I'm learning a whole bunch!" explained Angie. "I wouldn't trade it! Someday I'm planning to take over the business."

"Awesome!" said Ash, telling Angie about his plans to become a Pokémon Master.

Dawn and Brock piped up with their goals - to be a Top Coordinator and a Breeder. "I'll say one thing," smiled Angie. "You all dream really big!" As the kids laughed, the Camp teachers called for lights out… again.

Next morning Ash began the serious business of training Raichu.

The Pokémon's feeble Thunderbolt glanced off the rock it aimed at. When Ash chided Raichu, it simply dug another hole to hide in.

"You've gotta be strong to do this," coaxed Ash. "The only thing you need to have more of is confidence!"

Eventually Raichu agreed to try again. This time its Thunderbolt hit the spot, before an equally confident Focus Punch smashed the rock into pieces.

"You did it Raichu!" cheered Ash. "You just got in touch with your power!"

Angie, who'd been watching, began work on Monferno. Before long she was deftly dodging its Amber and Mach Punch moves, while shouting motivating words of encouragement.

At the end of the session Ash and Angie looked for each other.
"No offence Angie, but you look kinda beat up…" said Ash.
"Newsflash! So do you!" bristled a singed Angie. She pointed at Ash's hair that was sticking up on end from Raichu's electric shocks.
"Did you finally make friends with Monferno?" Ash asked.
"Yeah!" she said, tapping Monferno affectionately on the head. "We went at it and cleared the air!"
Ash explained that they'd solved Raichu's confidence problems.
"All our hard work'll pay off in today's battle, you'll see," he promised his new friend.
"If you're gonna beat someone it won't be us," taunted Angie.
"We'll see!" laughed Ash.

From the balcony of the school Dawn and Brock watched Ash and Angie's friendly rivalry.
"Now we just have to make sure that they don't beat us," said Brock.
"The only thing I'm thinking about is making Grimer shine like a star!" replied Dawn.
Professor Rowan joined the pals and watched as Ash and Angie tried to beat each other across the courtyard.
"They're the perfect example of Trainers who don't get along that well at first, but who end up as formidable rivals!" he declared.
"And that's what I love about this school."

The day of the Battle dawned brightly. Professor Rowan explained that the students should keep in mind the goal of battling so as to bring out the best in their Pokémon. First up was Brock versus Jessie.

"Now Magnemite. Thunder, let's go!' yelled Brock, ready for action.

Jessie couldn't get it together. First she tried coaxing Sweet Kiss from Smoochum, but it turned its powers on her. After she was sent crashing to the floor she gave up.

"My problem is with your terminal cuteness Smoochum," she said. "Now your Jessilinda can't bring herself to battle!" A 'No Contest' was called.

Next came Dawn and Conway.

"Grimer use Sludge!" called Dawn.

Conway pulled Venonat's Psychic move out of the bag, sending Grimer's sludge slopping back on him.

"Conway's totally in sync with that Venonat!" Brock whispered to Ash.

Dawn hung in there. When Venonat repelled her second attempt at Sludge, Grimer finished it off with Poison Gas.

"It's a V for Victory!" yelled Dawn.

"It's getting exciting!" said Conway as round two commenced.

Neither side wanted to give up. Finally, after pulling out move after awesome move with Grimer and Venonat, the pair shook hands to the cheers of their teams.

Finally the stage was set for Ash to battle Angie.

"We're up!" Ash told Raichu. "Just be confident and give it your all!"

Angie started with Monferno's Mach Punch. Ash countered with Pikachu's Focus Punch. The Pokémon clashed in mid-air. Angie called for Flamewheel. Ash responded with Dig and Raichu burrowed down just in time.

"Use Ember towards the hole," Angie commanded.

"Raichu, Dodge!"

"Monferno use Fury Swipes!"

"Raichu, Double Team! Now Thunderbolt!' The commands came thick and fast.

"Ash and Angie are sure getting heated!" exclaimed Dawn.
"What do you expect from a couple of hot heads?" replied Brock.
The fight continued with each Trainer urging their Pokémon to use better, stronger, faster moves. Raichu's final Thunderbolt and Monferno's Ember ended the fight in a huge explosion.
When the smoke finally cleared the Professor called time.
"Wow Raichu, you fought hard!" said Ash.
"You've all done very well working and battling with your Pokémon," said Rowan. "Now it's time to announce the student who most developed his or her relationship with their Pokémon…"
Everyone held their breath.
Professor Rowan smiled. "…it's Dawn!"
The place erupted in cheers.

"And after tallying up the total points, the team with the highest score is….'
Ash, Brock and Dawn watched nervously.
"… the Blue Team."
Conway laughed out loud. The Green Team came second, with Jessilinda deciding that their win was due to her Smoochum's cuteness.
"And coming in last is the Red Team," pronounced Rowan.
"But Dawn had the most points of anyone!" complained Angie.
"Although the Red Team battled valiantly they lost points because of yesterday's quarrelling coupled with that daytime nap."
Ash and Angie could do nothing but mouth apologies.
"I promise I'm gonna make it up!" said Ash.
"Yeah!" Angie agreed. "The battle's just begun."

Our Heroes' adventures at the Pokémon Summer Academy have only just started! Turn to page 44 to find out what other exciting activities await them.

DOUBLE VISION

IN THE STORY 'CAMPING IT UP!' ASH'S VICTORY OVER ANGIE WAS DOWN TO A COMBINATION OF ASH'S SKILL AS A TRAINER AND RAICHU'S POWERFUL MOVES. NOW ASH IS HELPING RAICHU TO MASTER DOUBLE TEAM. CAN YOU SEE HOW MANY TIMES THE ELECTRIC POKÉMON HAS MULTIPLIED ITSELF?

TREASURE CHEST MAKE-IT!

EVER WANTED SOMEWHERE SAFE TO KEEP YOUR POKÉMON TREASURES – ALL YOUR STICKERS, FIGURES OR DRAWINGS? NOW YOU CAN MAKE YOUR OWN PERSONAL STORAGE CHEST. JUST FOLLOW THESE EASY STEPS!

YOU WILL NEED:

A CEREAL BOX

PENCIL

SCISSORS

BROWN OR RED PAINT

PAINT BRUSH

SPLIT PIN

THICK YARN OR RIBBON

THIN CARD AND FELT TIP PENS (OPTIONAL)

PVA GLUE

1. Take a regular cereal box, lay it flat in front of you and turn it so the long, vertical sides are now horizontal. These will become the bottom and top of the chest, while the opening and bottom flap of the cereal box will become the sides. Draw a line in pencil across the horizontal box about three-quarters of the way up, extending it round to the sides.

2. Ask an adult to cut along the pencil line, so that the back is left untouched and the long side becomes the top of the chest.

3. Paint the outside of the chest in brown or red, then leave it to dry.

4. To make a clasp, use a pencil to mark a point on the front of the chest where the lid closes comfortably. Now push a split pin through the chest, opening the arms out inside so that it stays in place. Push a pencil through the lid of the chest at the point where the top part of the clasp should sit. Take a short piece of yarn or ribbon and push both ends through the hole, knotting them at the back. Adjust the ribbon at the front so that it is the right length to be looped around the split pin, holding the chest shut.

5. Cut-out the Pokémon logos and characters from this page, or trace their outlines and colour them in. Use the designs to decorate your chest, sticking the shapes wherever you like.

CAMP QUIZ

PART I

QUESTION 3

WHAT TYPE OF POKÉMON IS HIPPOWDON?

A. GRASS ☐

B. GROUND ☐

C. WATER ☐

QUESTION 2

SINNOH IS THE...

A. FOURTH REGION ASH HAS TRAVELLED THROUGH ☐

B. SECOND REGION ASH HAS TRAVELLED THROUGH ☐

C. SEVENTH REGION ASH HAS TRAVELLED THROUGH ☐

QUESTION 4

WHAT IS THE NAME OF THIS POKÉMON?

A. ABOMASNOW ☐

B. SNOVER ☐

C. GLACEON ☐

QUESTION 1

IN SINNOH, DAWN'S POKÉMON TRAVELLING COMPANION IS...

A. PIKACHU ☐

B. PACHIRISU ☐

C. PIPLUP ☐

QUESTION 5

ASH'S SURNAME IS...

A. KETCHUP ☐

B. KETTLE ☐

C. KETCHUM ☐

Not just anyone is accepted at Pokémon Training Camp. Professor Rowan carefully vets applicants and only chooses the crème de la crème of young Trainers, Breeders and Co-ordinators. Ash, Dawn and Brock made the grade, will you?

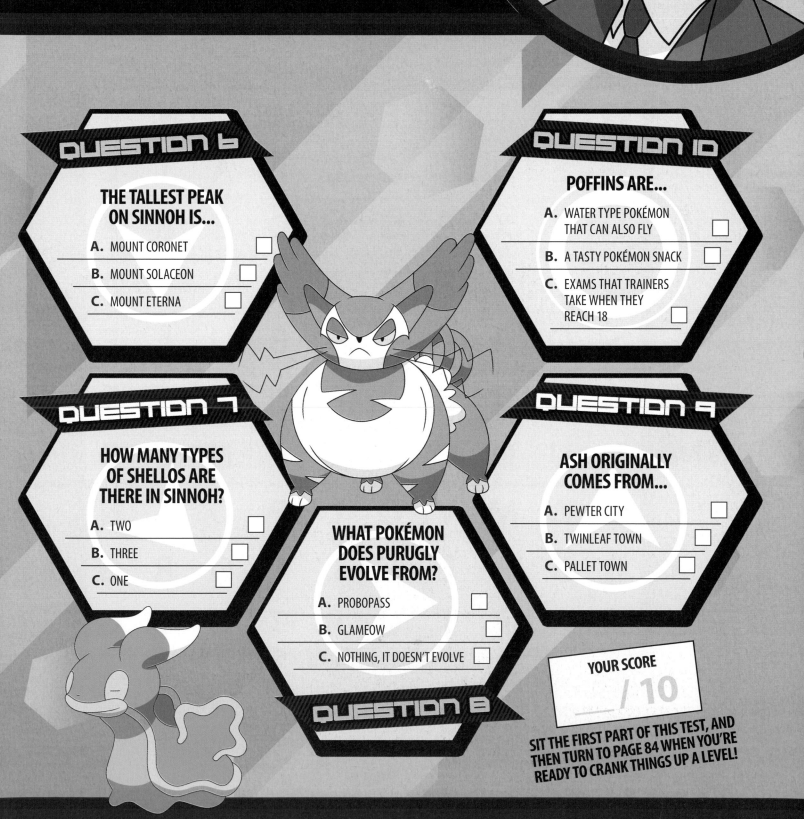

QUESTION 6

THE TALLEST PEAK ON SINNOH IS...

A. MOUNT CORONET ☐

B. MOUNT SOLACEON ☐

C. MOUNT ETERNA ☐

QUESTION 10

POFFINS ARE...

A. WATER TYPE POKÉMON THAT CAN ALSO FLY ☐

B. A TASTY POKÉMON SNACK ☐

C. EXAMS THAT TRAINERS TAKE WHEN THEY REACH 18 ☐

QUESTION 7

HOW MANY TYPES OF SHELLOS ARE THERE IN SINNOH?

A. TWO ☐

B. THREE ☐

C. ONE ☐

QUESTION 8

WHAT POKÉMON DOES PURUGLY EVOLVE FROM?

A. PROBOPASS ☐

B. GLAMEOW ☐

C. NOTHING, IT DOESN'T EVOLVE ☐

QUESTION 9

ASH ORIGINALLY COMES FROM...

A. PEWTER CITY ☐

B. TWINLEAF TOWN ☐

C. PALLET TOWN ☐

YOUR SCORE

/ 10

SIT THE FIRST PART OF THIS TEST, AND THEN TURN TO PAGE 84 WHEN YOU'RE READY TO CRANK THINGS UP A LEVEL!

GRASS-TYPE
WORD GRID

G	L	I	S	E	P	W	O	M	B
W	E	N	S	C	L	E	A	I	L
O	A	X	E	G	M	D	E	R	E
N	F	T	F	Z	A	U	R	R	A
S	O	A	I	M	R	B	U	E	F
A	N	B	R	U	Q	U	T	H	E
M	U	O	C	F	V	E	N	C	O
O	W	M	V	O	L	P	D	I	N
B	D	R	E	E	L	T	O	R	G
A	R	F	T	U	R	T	W	I	G

CAN YOU FIND WHICH GRASSY POKÉMON ARE GRAZING IN THE GRID ABOVE? THE NAMES OF THE SPECIES MAY BE HIDDEN VERTICALLY, HORIZONTALLY, DIAGONALLY OR EVEN IN REVERSE.

- ☐ ABOMASNOW
- ☐ BUDEW
- ☐ CHERRIM
- ☐ GROTLE
- ☐ LEAFEON
- ☐ SNOVER
- ☐ TURTWIG
- ☐ WORMADAM

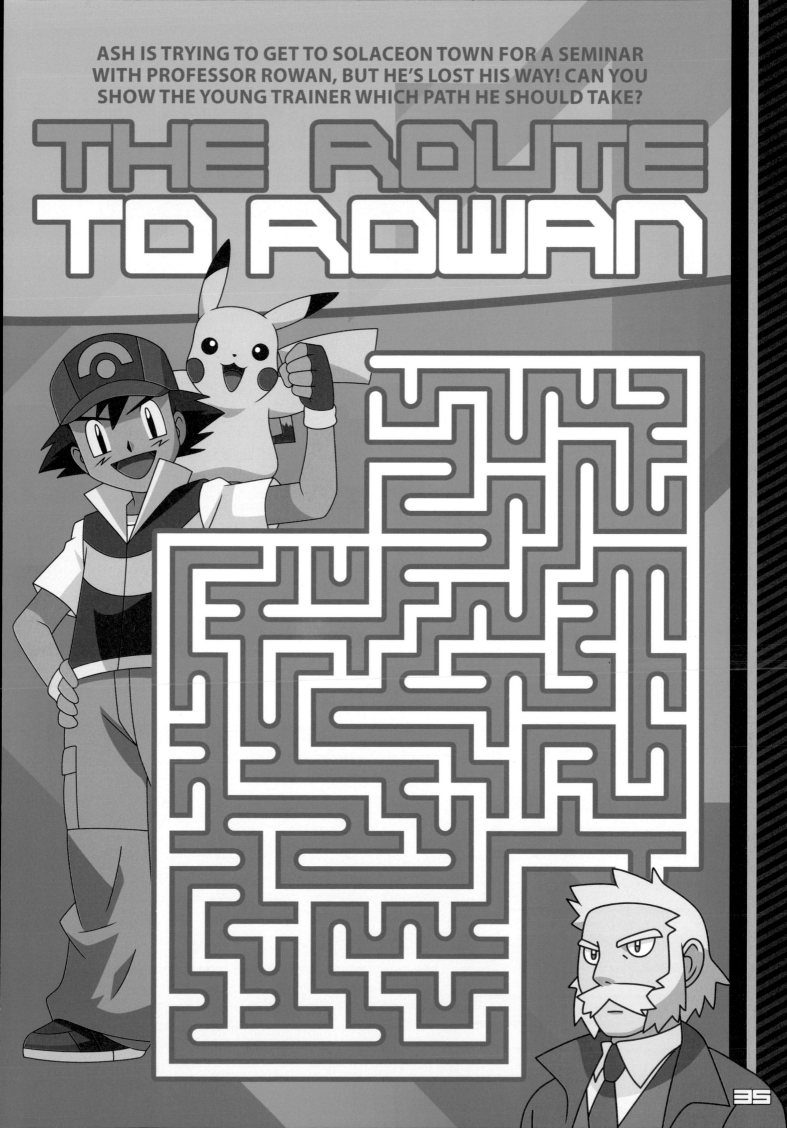

ASH IS TRYING TO GET TO SOLACEON TOWN FOR A SEMINAR WITH PROFESSOR ROWAN, BUT HE'S LOST HIS WAY! CAN YOU SHOW THE YOUNG TRAINER WHICH PATH HE SHOULD TAKE?

THE ROUTE TO ROWAN

NEW F

SHAYMIN

LAND FORME

TYPE:	GRASS
ABILITY:	NATURAL CURE
HEIGHT:	0.2m
WEIGHT:	2.1kg

SKY FORME

TYPE:	GRASS-FLYING
ABILITY:	SERENE GRACE
HEIGHT:	0.4m
WEIGHT:	5.2kg

Shaymin has two formes – the Land Forme looks rather like a small hedgehog and is quite shy, while the Sky Forme is bolder and deer-like in appearance. This Forme has also been known to challenge enemies that threaten its food or habitat. The gang came across a Sky Forme Shaymin in a meadow of flowers near Eterna City.

Shaymin is renowned in Sinnoh for its ability to transform spoiled urban areas into lush meadows. It is also able to breathe in dirty fumes and exhale fresh air. These unique qualities combined with its sweet nature make Shaymin universally adored. Dawn was particularly taken with its tiny form and sweet face. She is certain that it would do well in Contests.

ACES

Giratina is rarely sighted in Sinnoh, so the gang were particularly lucky to spot it. It is believed that this creature, a Ghost-Dragon type, lives in the Reverse World – a realm mirroring the world of Pokémon. Little is known about this parallel dimension, but it is said that Giratina appears there in its Origin Forme. In Sinnoh, the Pokémon manifests itself in its Altered Forme. Both states are extremely powerful, with Giratina wielding knife-like gold claws, pincers and a huge wingspan.

Sinnoh storytellers recount that a Shaymin once stumbled onto the path of a Giratina locked in battle with Dialga. The Giratina believed the ancient deity to have polluted its home and was enraged. The intensity of the combat between the two remarkable creatures created a noxious gas that lead Shaymin into the Reverse World. Despite its tiny size, Shaymin managed to escape by using its Seed Flare move to detoxify the gas. Now the two are linked in legend forever.

GIRATINA

ORIGIN FORME

TYPE:	GHOST-DRAGON
ABILITY:	LEVITATE
HEIGHT:	6.9m
WEIGHT:	650kg

ALTERED FORME

TYPE:	GHOST-DRAGON
ABILITY:	PRESSURE
HEIGHT:	4.5m
WEIGHT:	750kg

WHO GOES WHERE?

1) NEYSAHC

2) NAHSIMY

3) XION

4) SNEROV

5) EMLINOUN

6) OCKDULG

7) TELOGR

8) BIARELB

9) DEEDOUG

10) BELGI

Any Breeder worth their salt knows that the more information you have, the better equipped you are to deal with a hostile Pokémon encounter. Can you help Brock identify each of the Pokémon below? Unmuddle the anagrams then match them to the right Pokémon hideouts on the facing page.

1)

2)

3)

4)

5)

6)

7)

8)

9)

10)

☐ CAVES

☐ DAMS

☐ LAKES

☐ FOREST

☐ OCEAN FLOOR

☐ FLOWERY MEADOWS

☐ UNDERGROUND

☐ MOUNTAIN TRAILS

☐ HOSPITALS

☐ MOUNTAINS

LUMINEON

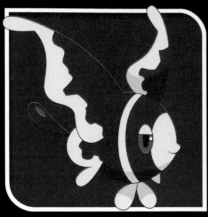

TYPE: WATER
ABILITY: SWIFT SWIM-STORM DRAIN
HEIGHT: 1.2m
WEIGHT: 24kg

Evolved from Finneon, Lumineon emits a blue glow from its tail fins, which can hypnotise and attract other Pokémon. This fish-like creature can only be found in the deepest parts of the ocean.

MAGIKARP

TYPE: WATER
ABILITY: SWIFT SWIM
HEIGHT: 0.9m
WEIGHT: 10.0kg

Despite its speed in the water Magikarp is said to be the world's weakest Pokémon. Its strange expression certainly makes it one of the least attractive. No-one knows how the Pokémon has managed to survive.

MAMOSWINE

TYPE: ICE-GROUND
ABILITY: OBLIVIOUS-SNOW CLOAK
HEIGHT: 2.5m
WEIGHT: 291.0kg

Swinub's third evolution has impressive tusks of ice. The population of Mamoswine thinned considerably when the climate turned warm after the Ice Age.

MANTYKE

TYPE: WATER-FLYING
ABILITY: SWIFT SWIM/WATER ABSORB
HEIGHT: 1.0m
WEIGHT: 65.0kg

This is a friendly Pokémon that can capture the subtle flows of seawater just by using its antennae. Mantyke eventually evolves into the elegant Mantine.

MISDREAVUS

TYPE: GHOST
ABILITY: LEVITATE
HEIGHT: 0.7m
WEIGHT: 1.0kg

This Ghost type has an unbearable shriek-like cry. Misdreavus evolves into Mismagius. It loves to entertain itself by sneaking up on people and then frightening them away.

MONFERNO

TYPE: FIRE-FIGHTING
ABILITY: BLAZE
HEIGHT: 0.9m
WEIGHT: 22.0kg

Monferno is evolved from Chimchar. It stretches out the flame of its fiery tail in order to appear bigger and more intimidating to would-be attackers.

MOTHIM

TYPE: BUG-FLYING

ABILITY: SWARM

HEIGHT: 0.9m

WEIGHT: 23.3kg

Mothim loves honey. In order to get its share of sweet treats, it frequently steals the nectar from Combee. The Bug-Flying Pokémon is evolved from Burmy, which has three types.

ONIX

TYPE: ROCK-GROUND

ABILITY: ROCK HEAD-STURDY

HEIGHT: 8.8m

WEIGHT: 210.0kg

A snake-like Pokémon which despite its bulk can move at up to 80 kilometres per hour. When it travels underground, Onix's size often creates tremors on the Earth's surface.

PACHIRISU

TYPE: ELECTRIC

ABILITY: RUN AWAY-PICKUP

HEIGHT: 0.4m

WEIGHT: 3.9kg

Pachirisu's cute squirrel-like exterior hides a dangerous opponent. It makes fur balls which crackle with static electricity. When living in the wild it stores them in tree holes.

PHIONE

TYPE: WATER

ABILITY: HYDRATION

HEIGHT: 0.4m

WEIGHT: 3.1kg

This is a Water type Pokémon that lives in warm seas. Phione inflates the flotation sac on its head when it's ready to drift and search for food. It has no evolutions.

PIKACHU

TYPE: ELECTRIC

ABILITY: STATIC

HEIGHT: 0.4m

WEIGHT: 6.0kg

Usually found in forests, Pikachu evolves into Raichu. It stores electricity in its cheek pouches, releasing it during attack with moves like Volt Tackle and Thunderbolt.

PIPLUP

TYPE: WATER

ABILITY: TORRENT

HEIGHT: 0.4m

WEIGHT: 5.2kg

The penguin-like Pokémon favoured by Dawn is a skilled swimmer and diver. Piplup dwells and hunts on the shores of the northern lakes, before evolving into Prinplup and the powerful Empoleon.

SINNOH EVIL

HIDING HERE IS A TRIO OF MISCHIEF-MAKERS WHO THRIVE ON COOKING UP PROBLEMS FOR ASH AND HIS FRIENDS. AS USUAL THEY'RE SURROUNDED BY SOME OF THEIR VILLAINOUS POKÉMON. JOIN THE DOTS TO DISCOVER WHO MAKES UP THIS BAD BUNCH.

UP CLOSE AND PERSONABLE!

With the first two exciting days of Pokémon Summer Academy behind them, our Heroes, along with all kinds of new friends and rivals are determinedly heading into Day Three…

"Today I'd like you to observe the Water-type Pokémon in this lake," Professor Rowan told his students. The young Pokémon pupils were grouped along the banks of a stunning expanse of water set against a backdrop of snow-covered mountains. "These waters are teeming with many kinds of Pokémon," explained the Professor's assistant. "Which ones to focus on are completely up to you." The assistant added that the students could work alone or in groups. The challenge was to express their findings in a report or sketch that would be graded on presentation.

Before sending them off, Professor Rowan had some last words of warning. "Because the Water-type Pokémon in this lake are still being researched, they are not allowed to be caught," he frowned. "Leaving the area is also forbidden. Our first priority is safety."

Ash, Dawn, Brock and Angie headed for a little jetty where two boats where moored.
"I'll bet those are a blast!" said Ash.
"They'd be a great way to observe Pokémon," agreed Dawn.
Angie nodded.
Ash was about to agree when he suddenly spotted a glowing blue light shining from the bushes on the other side of the lake.
"What's that?" he asked Pikachu, but his electric friend was walking towards the water's edge, as if in a trance.
"Hey!" shouted Ash. "You OK?"
The young Trainer placed a steadying hand on his Pokémon pal, bringing Pikachu back to reality.
"You were acting weird!" puzzled Ash. "I wonder what that light was?"

For now however there was no time to investigate, there was the more pressing matter of observing the Water-types and nailing the presentation.
"Hey Ash," asked Angie. "Wanna take a boat with me?"
The rivals were becoming good friends.
"Sure, let's go!" replied Ash, jumping in and starting the engine.
"Let's grab the other one," Brock suggested to Dawn.

Soon the foursome were speeding across the water as it sparkled in the sunlight.
On another boat Jessie, still disguised as Jessilinda, was letting others do all the hard work. Holding a parasol over head, she barked orders at two fellow students. "Smooth and steady as she goes men!" she gushed. "If you're extra smooth I'll let you observe my Water-type Pokémon for me."
The students nodded eagerly. "It will be an honour Miss Jessilinda."

Sitting on a bench on the bank her fellow Team Rocket members were making some observations of their own.
"Our Jessie certainly knows how to run a tight ship!" crowed James.
"With all those ocean liners named after queens I'm not surprised!" said Meowth.
"True," nodded James. "Though I fear our queen may have forgotten we've really come here to swipe the school's Pokémon."
Back on the lake the gang were having a ball, spotting ever more fabulous Pokémon.
"Wow! There's a Seel and a Poliwag," cried Ash.
"A Huntail and a Horsea!" noted Brock happily.
Just then Ash spotted a subject for his presentation.

"A Dewgong," he gasped. "…and a really healthy one too."
Shortly after a Sealeo broke the surface.
"That's the perfect choice for me," smiled Angie.

Meanwhile Dawn had spotted a Gorebyss. She was beside herself with excitement! The Co-ordinator was just about to get out her Pokédex when another boat bumped along side her. Suddenly Conway's voice pre-empted the machine's answer.

GOREBYSS
THE SOUTH SEA POKÉMON.
ITS LONG BEAUTIFUL PINK BODY IS MORE VIVID IN THE SPRINGTIME.

"What do you want?" said Dawn, annoyed at his interference. "To offer my help!" grinned Conway. "My encyclopaedic grasp of Pokémon is yours for the asking." Surprised and slightly creeped out by the offer, Dawn turned away and focused on the Gorebyss. "As for me…" decided Brock. "Chinchou!" The gang were all set.

In her boat Jessie was cracking the whip. "Have you decided which Pokémon you're going to observe for me?" she asked the boys in front. "Yes, Ms Jessilinda!" they answered dutifully. "We've decided on a Relicanth!" The students pointed at a plain brown and grey Pokémon swimming past them. "Ugh, that thing is so ugly it hurts my eyes!" screamed Jessie, recoiling. "I need a Pokémon that matches my beauty not insults it! I need a suave Suicune or a cute Manaphy." The boys tried to explain that the waters didn't hold those species, but Jessie was not listening. "Don't you bore me with details!" she shrieked at the terrified pair.

Across the lake, bickering had erupted between Ash and Angie again.
"You're blocking my view of the Dewgong!" yelled Ash.
"Well my Sealeo went the other way!" Angie huffed angrily.
The pair struggled for the controls, almost crushing poor Shinx who was nestling between their knees. Pikachu sighed in exasperation. For once Team Rocket were the calmer element, relaxing on their bench in the sunshine – Meowth and James had decided their Pokémon snatching plan could wait. Ash and Angie continued to snipe at each other, mocking each other's efforts to sketch the Pokémon they'd picked.
"That looks like a snowman to me," Ash grinned, pointing at Angie's Sealeo.
"Better a snowman than an alien," she replied, smirking at Ash's drawing of Dewgong.

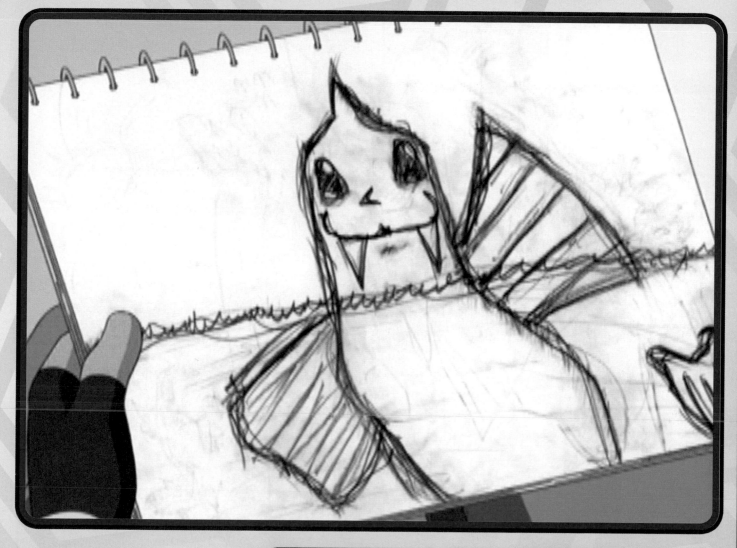

"If we give Professor Rowan these sketches we're going to flunk!" Ash said thoughtfully. "Maybe we should get closer to the Pokémon."
"I think you're on to something," smiled Angie. Within seconds the pair had dived in, followed by Brock and Dawn. Soon Piplup, Shinx and Pikachu were also bobbing about beside them.
"You've gotta be in the water to check out Water-types!" laughed Ash.

"The Gorebyss is even prettier underwater!" said Dawn.
"Chinchou give off electricity through their feelers, see," Brock told Angie, who jumped as shocks crackled from the Pokémon's antennae. But while the gang were making good headway, Jessie still hadn't got a Pokémon to study.
"Have you found a Pokémon that matches me in all my glory?" she asked her flunkies. "You bet!" the boys replied as a ferocious-looking Carvanha burst from the depths and jumped over the boat. Jessie screamed and fell back.
"Check out that aggression! How it looked just like it was gonna bite!" beamed the boys. "Just like you, don't ya think?"
"I think you're going to regret thinking," spat Jessie, her cheeks flaming with anger and humiliation.

Back in the water the gang were delighted to be getting up close and personal with their new Pokémon.
"I didn't know this Dewgong's horn was so hard," exclaimed Ash.
"I get it! You're using your nose to get to know me, aren't you?" said Angie as Sealeo rubbed its head against her.
"Chinchou really likes the flavour of this food!" chuckled Brock.
Dawn just couldn't get over Gorebyss' beauty. "Just gorgeous!" she giggled.

C onway quickly piped up. "Interesting! If that is in fact what happened then the legend may end up being true!"

"What legend?" asked Dawn.

"There's a famous legend that says that when a strange blue light flashes around this lake Pokémon start vanishing!"

The friends were horrified.

"Pokémon just vanish?" whispered Dawn in a trembling voice.

"Shinx disappearing may just have something to do with that legend," Conway continued.

Ash sprung into action.

"We've got to do something," he urged.

"I say we head over to where that light is coming from," agreed Angie.

"Hey folks, remember we're not allowed to go far from the lake…" Conway broke off before adding, "If Dawn's going I guess there's not much I can do."

Watching from the bushes James and Meowth had finally stopped snoozing in the sun and remembered their evil end goal.

"That flash has lots of zing!" smirked James.

"Ya mean like some treasure-type bling?" said Meowth, intrigued.

"I was thinking the same thing," chuckled James The pair began to stalk Ash and his friends through the undergrowth towards the bizarre light. As the gang reached a dark cavern, the weather broke and it began to rain.

"I'm quite confident that Shinx is around here!" announced Conway.

Dawn admitted she found the place creepy.

"No matter what happens I'll protect you," smiled Conway. At that moment a loud crash of thunder sent him running into the cave mouth for cover in very un-heroic fashion.

After an hour in the water the friends headed to the far bank for a sit-down.
"Let's observe them a little more and then get to work!" said Ash.
"When it comes to reports I'm the worst," whined Angie.
"No, I am!" said Ash.
"Nope, me!" cried Dawn.
Suddenly there he was again – Conway.
"Fear not Dawn!" he offered gallantly.
"I'd be happy to transcribe your thoughts!"

Dawn looked confused.
"It simply means that you do the talking and I'll write everything you say down and turn it into the perfect report!"
Blushing, Dawn spluttered that she felt she had to write the report herself
"As you wish," he sighed. "But if you change your mind, I'll be around,"
Conway's crush was now big enough to rival the type usually shown by Brock.

"Let's finish this up," said Ash, keen to get back to work.
Angie leapt to her feet. "Shinx is missing!"
"Piplup, weren't you and Shinx playing together?" Dawn asked her companion as the group called Shinx's name and searched the surrounding area. It appeared that Piplup wasn't listening. Instead the Penguin Pokémon was staring into the distance and moving off in a trance-like state. Ash recognised what was happening at once.
"There's that light again!" he said, pointing to a blue glow in the bushes.
"What do you mean 'again'?" Dawn asked.
"It flashed up earlier," explained Ash.
"What's wrong with you?" squealed Dawn, holding the hypnotised Piplup.
"The same result," Ash murmured. "First that light flashed and then Pikachu's eyes got all spacey."

Ash, Brock, Dawn and Angie joined Conway to shelter from the storm. Brock suggested they take a break, but Conway was pointing to the end of the cave that shone a bright green. "That's right," he remembered. "The legend states that the strange blue light comes forth from a green cave."
"That looks green to me," said Angie. Dawn was scared. "The light from the legend is back there!"
"Then we've got to go and look," replied Ash bravely.
The group set off towards the back of the cave, calling out Shinx's name as they walked. At the end of the tunnel the path opened out into a cavern with a lake. Stretching towards them in the water was the eerie blue light. "Don't look!" Ash yelled, panicking as Piplup became hypnotised. The Trainer clutched Pikachu to his chest.

Dawn snapped Piplup out of the trance but the light, still submerged in the lake, was heading in their direction. Suddenly there was a flash and a splash and a huge Water-type Pokémon with glowing fins burst into open air.
"So that's it!" breathed Angie. "This is where the strange blue light's been coming from!" gasped Ash.
"It's a Lumineon," explained Brock.
The details were reeled off once again from clever Conway before anyone could consult their Pokédex.
"Lumineon's beautiful," sighed Dawn, awestruck.

LUMINEON

LUMINEON LIVES IN THE OCEAN'S DEPTHS. IT LURES POKÉMON BY FLASHING LIGHT IN THE PATTERN OF ITS TAIL FINS.

As Conway and Brock discussed why Lumineon might be so far away from its natural habitat, the pit-pat of paws caught everyone's attention. There was Shinx! "I can't tell you how worried I was," Angie told her Pokémon, hugging it tightly. Now they had Shinx and knew the source of the bizarre light, most of the group felt that they could finally relax. Brock's brain cogs were still whirring however. "We have no idea why Lumineon's here! If we could get to the bottom of that, think what a great report we could do!" Before the friends could answer, trouble had arrived in the form of Jessie.

"I recognise you," said Conway. "It's Jessilinda, isn't it?" "It appears that I've finally found a Pokémon that matches me," she replied, as Ash and his friends glared at her. "That Lumineon is perfect for someone beautiful, elegant and refined like myself! Luring all kinds of Pokémon doesn't exactly hurt either. I'll catch it and then write a report… you can just go find something else." "It's against the rules to catch a Pokémon!" yelled Ash angrily. "I catch whatever I want to catch!" screamed Jessie. "That's my rule!" "We found that Lumineon first and you know it!" cried Angie indignantly. "Foolish talk from a loser," yelled Jessie, summoning Yanmega from her Poké Ball.

"If you don't mind, I'd like to handle this," said Conway calming the mood.
"Dawn," he smiled, calling forth Slowking.
"I'll wage this battle for you!"
Jessie was undaunted by this show of gallantry and nonplussed by Conway's choice of Pokémon.
"We're not the sharpest tool in the shed are we?" she grinned sarcastically.
"Over-confidence can be bad for your health," Conway replied coolly.
The Battle began.
"Yanmega!" called Jessie. "Use Sonic Boom!"
Conway instructed Slowking to use Protect, with great results.
"Slowking's Protect move is as strong as ever," said Dawn, psyched.
Even mid-battle, Conway was touched by her words. "How nice! I'm honoured you remembered that."

Next Slowking performed its Water Pulse move. Jessie countered with Steel Wing, but again Slowking's Protect repelled Yanmega.
"I'm too cute for this," screamed a frustrated Jessie.
Weakened and angry, it only took Conway and Slowking one more move to finish her and Yanmega off.
"That Psychic did the trick!" laughed Brock as Yanmega crashed on top of Jessie sending the pair rolling backwards into the tunnel. Luckily for her, James and Meowth were on hand to drag her away.
"I guess that blows the treasure concept!" said Meowth as he, James and Wobbuffet dragged Jessie away.
By the time the dust settled, there was no sign of 'Jessilinda' in the tunnel.
"She's probably very embarrassed right about now!" chuckled Dawn.

Ash brought everyone's thoughts back to their task.

"Let's observe the Lumineon!" he said, but as they turned back to the lake the Pokémon had gone.

"It may've gotten scared and hid underwater!" suggested Dawn.

Ash quickly summoned Buizel from his Poké Ball. "Will you help us look for the Lumineon?" he asked.

The pair dived into the water. Ash clung to Buizel's back as the Pokémon's tail propelled them silently through the lake. The Trainer kept his eyes peeled for the blue light, but it was nowhere to be seen.

"Find anything?" asked Dawn as Buizel and Ash resurfaced.

"Nope, Lumineon's gone," said Ash. "We did see a tunnel at the bottom of the lake though. It may have used that."

Brock suggested that as the tunnel was probably connected to the ocean, the Lumineon used it to travel to the cave from wherever it's living. The Breeder scouted for more clues as to why it would visit such a murky cave.

"That seaweed is a favourite of Water-type Pokémon," he said, pointing to some dark green moss covering the rocks. "It looks like a lot of it has been eaten. The thing is I don't see a trace of any other Pokémon here – so the Lumineon must be the one eating it all!"

Angie was impressed.

"Wow, excellent detective work!" agreed Conway.

"Anyone aiming to be a top Pokémon Breeder's gotta be smart!" said Ash proudly, patting his best friend on the back.

"We're going to give a great report!" gushed Dawn. She even gave Conway a hug when he repeated his offer of help.

Back at camp, the friends gave their presentation explaining how the Lumineon travelled to the cave from the ocean using an underwater tunnel. They also described how the fish-like creature's blue lights could attract Pokémon right to it. "I know because it lured my Shinx into the cave!" said Angie. "It affected Pikachu and Piplup too!' added Dawn. Brock summed up their findings by explaining that the Lumineon visited the cave in order to eat the seaweed. Their classmates cheered loudly. When Professor Rowan awarded them each a full ten points for their report, Ash and his pals jumped for joy.

It wasn't all good news however. "You all left the lake area without asking permission," boomed the Professor. "Have you any idea how worried we were?" Four points were deducted from each score. "Now you know you can't just do what you want,"

said Jessie smugly. "Excuse me," said the Professor's assistant, cutting Jessie down to size. "Since you left the lake too you lose four points as well!" Conway also lost four points, but he seemed relieved it wasn't more. The students ended their day with a slightly less

exciting exercise – cleaning the school corridors. "We got a perfect score, but we still had four points taken off," groaned Ash. "Look at the bright side," said Angie. "We got to see Lumineon." Ash smiled. "I sure hope we get to see it again."

And with the completion of Day Three, Pokémon Summer Academy continues. Turn to page 66 for the next thrilling instalment!

WAY TO WORK IT OUT!

Being a Pokémon Trainer is not all about physical strength. You've got to have strength of mind too!

Flex some mental muscle and give your brain cells a workout with this word puzzle. See how many words of at least three letters than you can form out of the phrase below. You're up against a time deadline of three minutes!

ASH KETCHUM AND PIKACHU NEVER GIVE UP

1.	21.
2.	22.
3.	23.
4.	24.
5.	25.
6.	26.
7.	27.
8.	28.
9.	29.
10.	30.
11.	31.
12.	32.
13.	33.
14.	34.
15.	35.
16.	36.
17.	37.
18.	38.
19.	39.
20.	40.

EVOLUTION SOLUTIONS

Dawn has come across some new Pokémon! She wants to research them on her Pokédex, but a Bubblebeam move from Piplup has temporarily short-circuited it. Can you help by naming the missing evolution in each chain?

1 DRIFLOON

_ _ _ _ _ _ _ _ _

2 YANMA

_ _ _ _ _ _ _ _

3

_ _ _ _ _ _

_ _ _ _ _ _ _ _

4 PORYGON

PORYGON 2

_ _ _ _ _ _ _ - _

5

_ _ _ _ _ _

_ _ _ _ _ _

LUXRAY

6 GIBLE

_ _ _ _ _ _

_ _ _ _ _ _ _ _

CODED CORRESPONDENCE

H__ __ng__,

H_w _s _t g__ng? _ h_p_
b_th y__ _nd Sh_nx _r_ w_ll?
_r_ th_ngs b_sy _t th_
P_k_m_n D_y c_r_
c_ntr_? D_wn, Br_ck
_nd _ _r_ r___lly
m_ss_ng y__. W_
c_n't b_l__v_ w_ h_v_
t_ w__t _ wh_l_ y__r
b_f_r_ th_ n_xt c_mp.
W_'r_ _ff t_ __r n_xt
Gym, b_t w_'ll try t_ v_s_t
r__l s__n.
L_v_

_sh

Ash has made a firm friend and a rival to be reckoned in Angie. Now the pair have become pen pals. With Team Rocket always spying on their movements, the pals have taken to communicating in code. Can you use your skill and knowledge of Pokémon to work out what the letters say? Look at the Key code – each Pokémon corresponds to the vowel that begins its name.

Once you've worked out which Pokémon stands for each vowel, read the letter substituting the pictures for the correct letters.

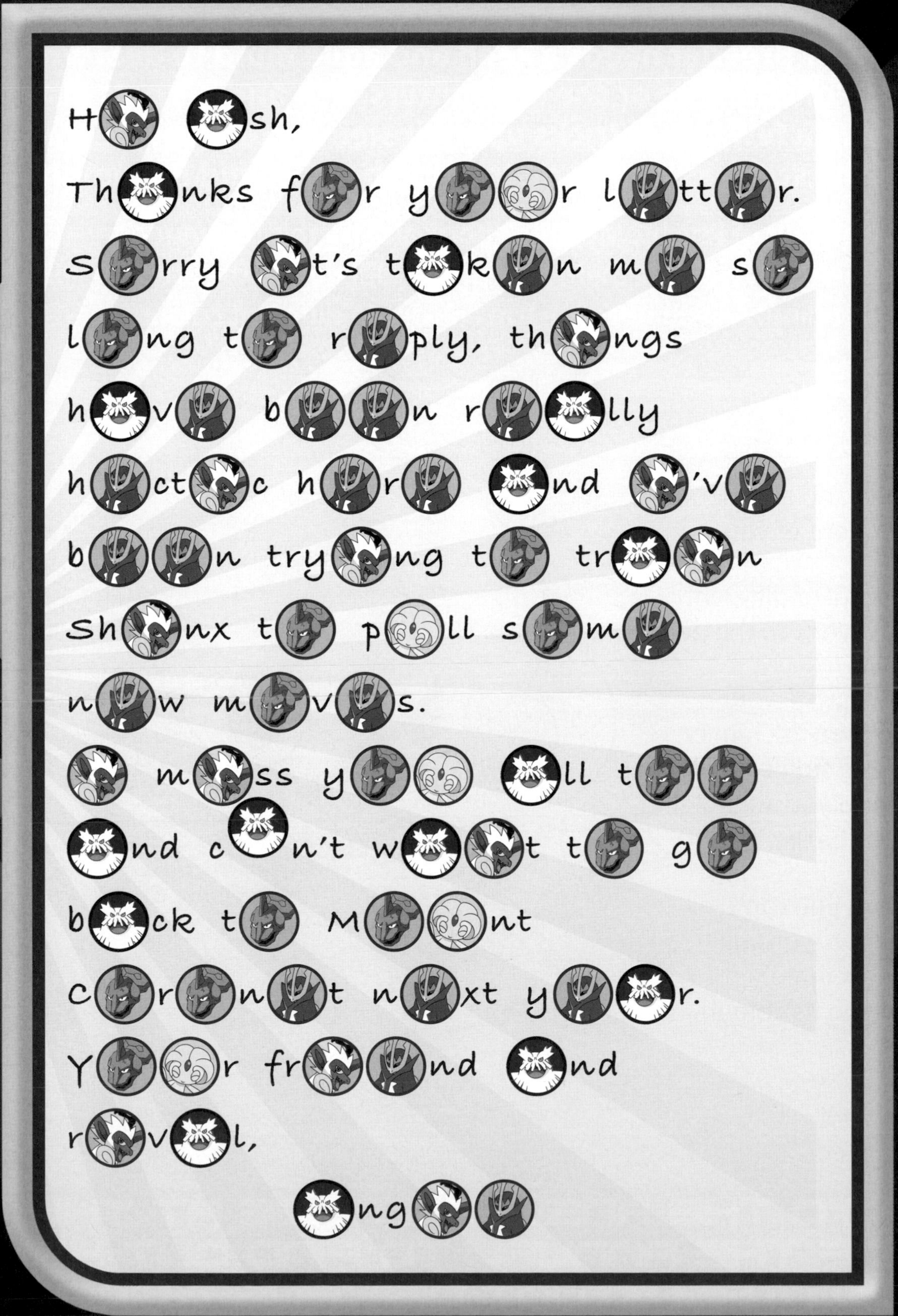

Hi Ash,

Thanks for your letter. Sorry it's taken me so long to reply, things have been really hectic here and I've been trying to train Shinx to pull some new moves.

I miss you all too and can't wait to go back to Mount Coronet next year. Your friend and rival,

Angie

CODE KEY

MEDITITE'S MIND-READING

A top Trainer or Breeder needs a keen and agile mind to deal with the Psychic Pokémon he or she encounters. Ash and his pals also have to have a few clever tricks up their sleeves to throw Team Rocket off the scent as well as distracting hostile wild Pokémon.

Take a leaf out of Psychic Meditite's book and try this trick out on your friends. It will give them a great introduction to the art of mind-reading! All you need are five crayons in different colours.

- Pick a friend and ask them to stand in front of you.

- Give a handful of different coloured crayons to the person.

- Turn your back on your friend and then ask him or her to place a single crayon into the hand you are holding behind your back.

- Even though you can't see the crayon, you will be able to accurately tell the person its colour!

TURN TO THE ANSWERS PAGE AT THE BACK OF THE ANNUAL TO FIND OUT HOW TO PULL THIS STUNT OFF EVERY TIME!

SWEET SHADOWS

As ferocious and frightening as some species of Pokémon are, there are as many who have what Jessie calls 'the cute factor'. Here are the shadows of some of the sweetest sorts around. Can you work out who's who and then label them? We've given you the first and last letters as a clue.

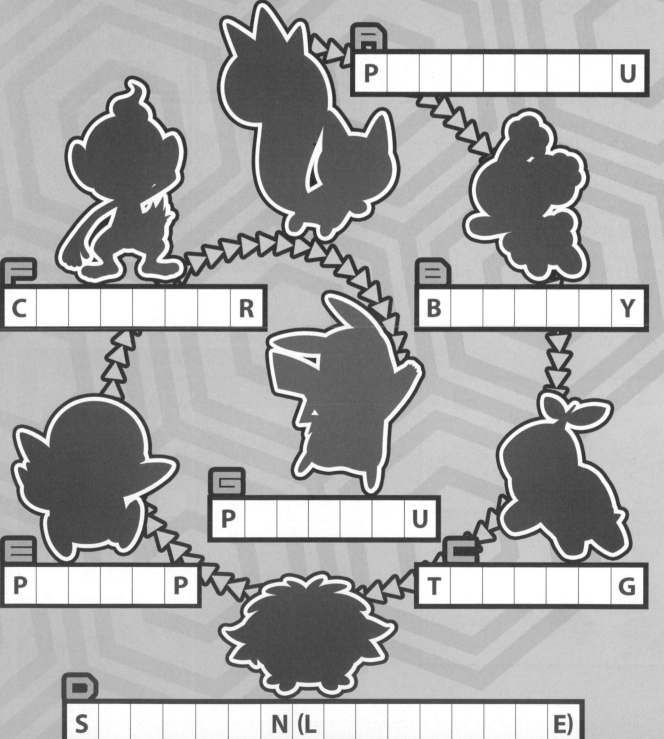

P _ _ _ _ _ _ U

C _ _ _ _ _ _ R

B _ _ _ _ _ Y

P _ _ _ _ _ P

G
P _ _ _ _ U

C
T _ _ _ G

D
S _ _ _ _ N (L _ _ _ _ E)

BROCK'S

SATISFY YOUR COMPETITIVE STREAK WITH BROCK'S COOL BINGO GAME!

YOU WILL NEED:

2 TO 4 PLAYERS

A DICE

PENCILS OR PENS

HOW TO PLAY:

First choose a playing grid each. Throw the dice to see who goes first, with the highest number starting. The first player must roll the dice and find the picture at the top of the page that corresponds with the number rolled. If the player has that same picture on their card, they can cross it off. Play then passes to the next person. When a player has crossed off all their pictures they have to shout 'Pokémon'! The first person to shout out wins.

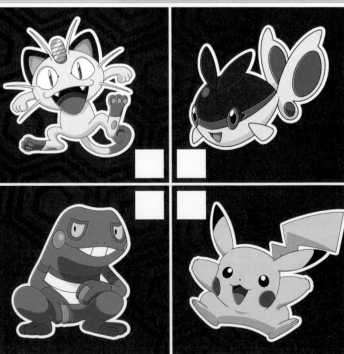

BINGO

PLAYER 3

PLAYER 4

WATER COMES NEXT?

These Water types are practising for the swim section of the Pokémon Triathlon. Study the relay pattern in each line, then work out who's swimming the next leg. Can you draw the right Pokémon in place each time?

1)

2)

3)

4)

GHOUL DAZE!

It's Day Five of the Pokémon Summer Academy and everyone's raring to go. With all the amazing things they've been learning, our Heroes and their new friends can't help but wonder what's in store...

Ash and his friends were in the classroom when they heard the familiar voice of Professor Rowan booming over the airwaves. "Today's activities will deal with the proper way to interact with Ghost-Type Pokémon," he announced. Everyone fell into shocked silence. Brock and

Dawn glanced at each other in amazement. "The goal of this programme is to ensure that you will be able to correctly approach Ghost Pokémon, whenever or wherever you encounter them', continued the Professor before signing off and handing over to the instructor standing at the blackboard in front of them.

"Let's go over the rules," said the Professor's assistant. "After each of you teams up with a fellow classmate, you will go together to retrieve this medal from the Summit Ruins. Your final score will be based on how long it takes you. The event begins tonight at seven sharp, so your job right now is to find a partner!" "It sounds to me like this is a test of courage," said Brock. "OK Pikachu, are you up for this?" Ash asked his trusty companion, who as usual was perched on his shoulder.

CAMP CROSSWORD

How would you survive at Summer Academy? Professor Rowan believes the best students are alert, quick-thinking and passionate about building their Pokémon knowledge. See how quickly you can fill in this tricky crossword, using the clues below to help you.

ACROSS

1. Weak and unpopular Water-type Pokémon.
2. Budding Breeder who loves to cook.
3. The cute Pokémon that Jessie couldn't bear to battle with.
4. A species that becomes aggressive if it stores too much electricity without release.
5. A cool move employed by number 3 Down.

DOWN

1. Meowth's Rocket crew.
2. Mountain location of Rowan's Research facility and the highest point on Sinnoh.
3. Flying Pokémon often favoured by Ash
4. Gabite's evolution.
5. The name of the Sludge Pokémon.

Outside everyone began thinking hard about which student they'd like to work with. "Who're we going to pair with?" Ash asked Pikachu.
Just then Shinx appeared and the two Pokémon lovingly greeted each other. Angie wasn't far behind.
"Since Pikachu and Shinx get along so well, why don't we be partners?" she asked Ash. The wannabe Trainer jumped at the chance.

"We'll mop the floor with every last one of those guys!" Angie continued, as the two did a cool handshake.
In another area of the courtyard a small boy called Mitchell timidly approached Brock. "Uh Brock…" he stuttered shyly. "The thing is I'm kind of scared of the dark. So I was wondering if you'd be my partner?"
To Mitchell's amazement and delight, the kind Breeder immediately agreed.

"What?! You two guys have partners already?" Dawn cried when Ash and Brock explained that they were already paired with Angie and Mitchell. "It just happened that way!" said Brock to Dawn, who was visibly anxious about who was left to partner.
Suddenly she felt a huge presence approach. "Weird!" she whispered. "I've got a feeling that something really gross is standing right behind me."
"Hey Dawn!"
The Co-ordinator span on her heels to see Kendall, a burly beefcake who loved to show off his physique.
"Any idea what these biceps are for?" he preened, showing off his huge arm muscles. "When you're scared out of your wits and wanna run away, they'll be there to stop you."

Kendall was convinced he was making an offer that Dawn couldn't refuse. Without any other options on the table, she had little choice but to accept.

Elsewhere in the compound Conway was considering who he should choose, unaware that his crush, Dawn, was spoken for. Suddenly he heard a ghostly laugh and saw an arm beckoning him from the bushes beside the path. A petite girl popped out and smiled at him. "So you're on the Blue Team too and don't have a partner?" Conway asked, confused. The girl nodded. "Let's play," she said in a mesmerising tone. She looked Conway in the eye and he instantly fell under her spooky spell. Jessie meanwhile was in the process of picking her own partner – or should that be servant – from a group of four eager boys in the Green Team. "Ms Jessilinda actually chose me!" crowed the winner. The bespectacled lad had no idea what he was in for.

"Fast times means big points," said Jessie as she snuck behind the building to meet James and Meowth. "No goofy Ghost Pokémon will keep me from smoking the competition!" The hapless pair were still disguised as maintenance men. "You want us to rig the programme and toss you the win?" asked James. "I do, and thank you for your support," Jessie admitted dryly. "We can't rustle up a robot without cash," Meowth protested. "Cash, shmash" said Jessie, explaining that she wanted the pair to dress up as Ghost Pokémon themselves, not design a robotic one. Meowth was not amused. "I don't even know, much less look like, a Ghostie Pokémon," he meowed. "Calm those whiskers," Jessie soothed. "A nip here and a tuck there and you'll make lovely Ghost Pokémon!" "In whose dreams?" raged Meowth.

At precisely 7pm the students congregated at the starting point in the dark woods. They nervously clutched their torches while Professor Rowan explained that each team would depart from different locations, all the same distance away from the ruins.

The Red Team, including Ash and Angie, Brock and Dawn and their partners would depart first.
"All right," came the announcement.
"On your marks!"
Ash and Angie set off at a pace.
"That number one spot is ours!" Ash told Angie.

The pair continued through the dark forest.
"There's something creepy about this place," admitted Ash.
"Let me know if you're scared," Angie reassured him.
"Same goes for you," replied Ash boldly. "Don't go running off on me."
Suddenly some ghoulish eyes gleamed red in the bushes, startling Pikachu and Shinx! A huge metal hand belonging to a Haunter lurched forward and grabbed Shinx's tail. Pikachu immediately let off a Volt Tackle until the hand let go of his friend.

Ash went to investigate.

"Hey it's just some Ghost Pokémon," he said, before apologising to the Gastly, Haunter and Gengar who were hiding in the bushes.

"Pikachu next time, why don't you count to ten?" he told his companion.

"Pikachu was only trying to protect Shinx for us," Angie gently pointed out.

"I guess so," said Ash. "Let's move on."

Back at the start the Professor was setting off the next duo – Brock and Mitchell.

"Keep an eye out for me," stammered Mitchell. "Won't you Brock?"

"Of course, I will," Brock smiled.

As they left Dawn and Kendall stepped up to the start line. For some reason Dawn's new buddy seemed very jumpy.

In another part of the forest a student ran up to the teachers at the Blue Team gate.

"I'm late because I must've dozed off," she explained.

The confused teachers had already seen all five Blue Team couples set off. They double-checked their lists.

"All ten of the Blue Team students are on their way to the ruins already," said one frantically.

"That means there are eleven students!"

Who was the mysterious extra Blue Team member? Deep in the forest Mitchell had stumbled on the same trio of Ghost Pokémon who had freaked out Shinx earlier on.

"Relax," soothed Brock. "I've got just the thing for them."

The kind Breeder brought out a delicious bag of food.

"Hey fellas check this out!" said Brock to Gastly, Haunter and Gengar. "You're gonna love this!" he continued. "I made it just for you. Super special Ghost Pokémon food!" The three Pokémon fell on the food and began eating merrily.

"You're a genius Brock!" said Mitchell, who was just as impressed as he was relieved. The pair continued on their way as the sound of happy crunching faded into the distance.

"Listen! What's that noise?" Dawn asked Kendall who, since entering the forest had been cowering behind her back. "Sounds like monsters eating something!" squeaked the cowardly giant. Suddenly deciding he could take it no more, the terrified muscle man stood up and turned back. "It's not going to be meeeeeee!" he cried, dashing off. "Kendall, hold on!" Dawn bellowed after him. She'd discovered the Ghost Pokémon crunching up Brock's food. The news came too late – Kendall was already a speck in the distance. "He can talk the talk, but he sure can't walk the walk," Dawn sighed to Piplup.

Hearing a rustle in the bushes, Dawn looked round. She could see Conway, but he was alone. "No partner?" she said, continuing on her path. "Wonder what that's all about?" Over on his trail, Conway was still in a bewitched state. "This way, over here," called the girl's eerie voice. Conway obeyed, echoing her words. When the girl reached the edge of a cliff, instead of falling she floated into the air over the drop. She called out to Conway and he blindly followed her. When he reached the edge he began to plummet to his death, until a huge metal arm grabbed hold of him and pulled him back to safety. The ghostly girl vanished into thin air. The arm belonged to a Dusknoir. "You scared me!" said Conway, waking from his trance. Dusknoir responded with a deafening roar. This latest ordeal was too much for poor Conway. The student screamed and fainted.

Hearing the noise, Dawn rushed to find her new friend. She gasped when she came across Dusknoir floating next to Conway's unconscious figure. Instead of fleeing, the plucky Co-ordinator challenged the Pokémon. "All right," she yelled. "What did you do to Conway?" Dusknoir floated into the air and he too vanished. After a few minutes Dawn managed to rouse Conway and check her Pokédex.

DUSKNOIR

IT RECEIVES ELECTRICAL WAVES FROM THE SPIRIT WORLD WITH ITS ANTENNA AND IS SAID TO TAKE PEOPLE TO THE SPIRIT WORLD AS WELL.

"A few more steps and I would've ended up in the Spirit World too!" croaked Conway, asking where the girl he'd been following was. He was amazed when Dawn revealed he'd been alone the whole time. "You don't think Dusknoir took her to the Spirit World do you?" asked Dawn.

Hiding in the undergrowth Meowth had had enough of waiting in his ghostly get up. "Man, this Ghost Pokémon gig can bore the sheets off ya," he whined. Suddenly he spotted torch beams. "Here's where this scarin' gig gets good!" he whispered, putting on his ghost mask. Unfortunately however he managed to catch his face in the zipper. "People have been tellin' me to zip my lips all my Pokémonic life," he yelped. "But now I really did it!" Meowth fell backwards just as Ash and Angie passed. By the time he'd got up again the pair had gone.

Meowth was furious.
"They split!" he groaned. "And here I am with my chops caught in this zipper!" Luckily for Meowth someone or something else was on hand to unzip his costume. "You helped me save face! Thank you!" he cried looking upwards to see who or what had sorted him out.
"It's the real deal!" he suddenly screamed, catching sight of an actual Banette. It looked the same as the costume he'd been sporting. More Ghost types, Shuppet and Duskull, were floating above it. "They're going to turn me into Monster Mash," he screamed, running for his life.

Meowth ran so fast, he tripped and rolled down a big hill. As he went bits of disguise were scattered in all directions. No sooner had he picked himself up than he felt a presence behind him. "My creepy meter's ringing off the charts!" he said, looking round to see the ghostly girl who'd bewitched Conway. "Want some?" she asked, offering Meowth a fried cake ball skewer. The Pokémon leapt forwards greedily, but the girl was playing a ghostly game. As Meowth pounced on the food she floated backwards, forcing him to follow her further and further into the trees.

Just as he was about to follow for a third time, Meowth felt a steel hand grasp his arm and hold him back. "Hey I was closing in on some serious chow!" he screeched. Meowth whipped round to see Dusknoir looming dangerously above him. The shocked Pokémon opened his mouth and screamed. "Was that a bloodcurdling scream?" Jessie asked her partner matter-of-factly, urging him to investigate. "That looks like a Meowth," the boy called back to Jessie, his torchlight falling on a Pokémon lying on the ground. For once, Jessie seemed genuinely shocked to see her Team Rocket pal hurt. "Rise and shine!" she said in a panicky voice, shaking Meowth violently in an attempt to wake him up.

Meowth barely had time to open his eyes before Dusknoir loomed into view again, bellowing its deafening roar. All thoughts of Meowth's well-being vanished from Jessie's head as she hurried to save her own skin. "You schlep that Meowth with you and I'll pull you two along in my wake!" she cried to her partner. Jessie belted off through the trees, leaving the small boy to lumber behind with Meowth in his arms.

Soon the fleeing group passed Brock and Mitchell. "It's here!" screamed Jessie to the confused pair. Seconds later they saw what 'it' was. "Don't worry," said Brock "I still have some Ghost Pokémon food." Unfortunately the Breeder's offering just seemed to enrage Dusknoir. "I think we'd better go!' Brock decided.

Meanwhile Ash and Angie, unaware of the chaos further down the mountain, had almost reached the Summit Ruins. "Did you hear that Angie?" asked Ash. Angie nodded as a weird moaning noise filled the air. "Sounds like it's coming from the rock!" said Ash. "But how?" wondered Angie. Suddenly they got their answer. A Misdreavus materialised in front of the duo's eyes. The pair were so shocked they fell down, but worse was to come when the Ghost Pokémon began to emit its high-pitched shrieking sound waves. "It's killing my ears," called Angie as they ran off. Once out of range they began arguing about who'd wimped out first, until they realised that they'd got horribly lost. "Come this way," called an eerie voice. The ghostly girl was beckoning…

Having reached the safety of the school, Jessie, Brock, Dawn and Mitchell were busy telling the teachers about the Dusknoir they'd spotted.

"That's strange," said Professor Rowan. "We monitor every Pokémon in this area but we don't have any record of a Dusknoir dwelling here."

"What do you think that Dusknoir's doing here?" asked Dawn.

"Well, an accident did take place the other day," the Professor murmured. He told the group how they'd been doing renovations when they discovered a cave deep within a stone wall. "There are some who think it might be the legendary entrance to the Spirit World, he mused, adding "It's possible that Dusknoir's attempting to take someone back with it."

"I have reason to believe it may have already abducted a girl," said Conway.

Up at the summit Ash and Angie found the girl had led them directly to the ruins. Among the stones they found the medals. "We found the Summit Ruins first... we got the Summit Ruins Medal!" they shouted, hugging each other.

Their joyful celebrations were cut short by the sound of the mysterious calling girl. The friends eventually found her at the entrance to a huge rock.
"Is there something in there?" Ash asked her.
"Yes," she breathed. "Let's go together."

The pair took one step forward before Dusknoir floated down, blocking their path. It gave a deafening roar. "Check it out!" yelled Ash above the noise, out of interest as much as fear. "It's a Dusknoir!" Angie cried. At their feet Pikachu was crackling with electricity while Shinx began to spit furiously. Sensing attack, Dusknoir unleashed a terrible move. "Was that a Psychic Attack?" croaked Angie after the dust had cleared.

Shinx and Pikachu struggled but they were bound completely by Dusknoir's Psychic energy. Ash and Angie could do nothing but watch in horror as Dusknoir turned its attentions towards the little girl near the rocks. "She's gonna get hurt!" screamed Angie, trying to dodge round Dusknoir and free the girl. The Dusknoir pre-empted this – soon Angie and Ash were bound by its energy along with their Pokémon.

After what seemed like hours Shinx and Pikachu finally mustered the power to escape Dusknoir's energy hold. With amazing resilience the two Pokémon, dwarfed by the huge Ghost-Type, struggled to their feet.
"Pikachu," urged Ash. "Quick, Volt Tackle!"
"Shinx, use Thunder Fang, go!" cried Angie.
Shinx and Pikachu leapt forward, both sparking with electricity.

The pair threw themselves at Dusknoir, who, still heading for the girl, was taken by surprise. There was an almighty explosion and an enormous thud as Dusknoir crashed to the ground, lifeless.
"All right!" yelled Ash, jumping for joy as he saw the amazing feat his trusty Pokémon friends had pulled off. The tiny twosome had actually managed to fell the giant, metal Ghost-Type.

They literally couldn't believe their eyes.
At that instant Ash noticed the girl. With a weird smile she began beckoning again.
"Let's play now," she murmured. "Let's play now."
"Now's no time for play," Ash called.
"That Dusknoir's going to wake up any minute," added Angie, beckoning for the girl to come away from the rocks.

But the girl wasn't listening "I want you all to come with me," she repeated over and over again. Just then, the hole behind her began filling with swirling, purple colours.

It was impossible to tell if it was smoke or light. "Whoa, what's that?" asked Ash. He didn't have long to wonder. A furious hurricane began blowing and a huge force began sucking them all towards the gaping hole. Ash managed to hold on to Angie's hand, but he too began sliding towards the fissure. Pikachu and Shinx were only kept safe because they were clutching on to his trouser leg.

The situation was becoming critical. Ash didn't know how much longer he could hold on. "Angie!" he called in terror. "Just don't let go of my hand!" "I won't!" cried the brave Trainer, who was by this time parallel with the ground. Angie realised that she was just centimetres from the opening the cave. The girl stood motionless at the opening, despite the hurricane raging about her. Suddenly she let forth a high-pitched and sinister laugh. "Let's play," she cackled evilly. "Ash, it's no use!" called Angie, whose grip was loosening. "Just let me go. "I'll never give up!" Ash cried through gritted teeth.

At that point the teachers ran into the clearing nearby. Professor Rowan surveyed the scene and held everybody back. "Is that the Spirit World entrance?" his assistant asked. "I think someone's trying to pull them in!" cried Brock. "We've got to do something!" yelled Dawn.
The Professor refused to let them put themselves in danger.
"Let's play," repeated the girl's evil call.
Everything seemed lost.
Ash could no longer hold on to Angie but then, unbelievably Dusknoir swooped in. The great hulk of metal grabbed both Ash and Angie, before anchoring itself into the ground. "Dusknoir, you're trying to save us!" exclaimed Angie in surprise.

For a few moments it looked as if even Dusknoir's size and bulk wouldn't save them.
"We're gonna be sucked in!" screamed Angie.
With a massive roar Dusknoir summoned a ball of energy that it directed straight at the mouth of the cave. It hit the little girl, bowling her backwards straight into the Spirit World. The colours faded, the wind died and the cave entrance filled up with rocks.

"You were looking out for us all along weren't you?" marvelled Angie, thanking the Ghost Pokémon.
"You're awesome," added Ash, as Dusknoir evaporated into thin air once more.

Back at the school both students and teachers tried to make sense of what had happened. "Was that really the entrance to the Spirit World?" Angie asked. Professor Rowan admitted that he didn't know. "It's obvious Dusknoir had a vested interest in guarding it," he pointed out. "But the fact is scientists still have a very long way to go before we truly understand our world and theirs." Something was still bugging Conway. "Does that mean that the girl I was partnered with wasn't in the Academy?" he asked. "I seriously doubt that she was part of this world," said the teaching assistant. The idea of being partnered with a ghost was enough to totally freak Conway out, much to everyone else's amusement.

Finally it was down to the business of results. "We had a busy night, but you all performed admirably," smiled the Professor. "So I've decided to give each team thirty points!" As usual Jessie wasn't happy. "Now what kind of communal drivel is that?" she moaned. Brock on the other hand was delighted. "That means we still stay in second place!" "For the Blue Team it's definitely lonely at the top!" chuckled Conway. Always ready to rise to the challenge, Ash was in a motivating mood. "Listen up!" he told his Red Team members. "Let's get on this stick and turn this thing around!" His words were met with excited cheers and much enthusiasm.

So as the end of the Summer Academy draws near…the subject of our Heroes' last assignment remains a mystery! Will Ash and Friends make a comeback? Turn to page 88.

CREEPY
COLOUR-IN

Welcome to level two of the entrance examination for Pokémon Camp. Professor Rowan is busy compiling his list of candidates who have won coveted places on the course. Will your name be on the scroll? Take the test then turn to page 104 for the final part.

QUESTION 6

SHAYMIN'S MORE TIMID FORME IS...

A. LAND FORME ☐

B. SKY FORME ☐

C. NEITHER, IT IS ALWAYS BOLD AND FRIENDLY ☐

QUESTION 7

MAMOSWINE'S IMPRESSIVE TUSKS ARE MADE OF

A. STONE ☐

B. ICE ☐

C. BONE ☐

QUESTION 8

ICE-TYPE SNORUNT CAN EVOLVE INTO FROSLASS, BUT WHAT IS ITS OTHER PARALLEL EVOLUTION?

A. FEEBAS ☐

B. GLACEON ☐

C. GLALIE ☐

QUESTION 10

GALLADE'S MAIN WEAPON IN BATTLE IS...

A. A HORNY CREST ON ITS HEAD WITH WHICH IT HEAD-BUTTS ENEMIES ☐

B. SWORDS EXTENDING FROM ITS ELBOWS ☐

C. ITS PIERCING RED-EYED GAZE THAT DISTRACTS ENEMIES ☐

QUESTION 9

TEAM ROCKET OFTEN TRAVEL BY...

A. HOT AIR BALLOON ☐

B. AIRSHIP ☐

C. MOTORCYCLE AND SIDE-CAR ☐

YOUR SCORE

___ / 20

SIT THE SECOND PART OF THIS TEST, AND THEN TURN TO PAGE 104 WHEN YOU'RE READY TO CRANK THINGS UP A LEVEL!

PORYGON-Z

TYPE: NORMAL
ABILITY: ADAPTABILITY-DOWNLOAD
HEIGHT: 0.9m
WEIGHT: 34.0kg

Additional software was installed to make Porygon-z a more effective Pokémon. It began acting oddly afterwards, however. This is the third evolution in the Porygon chain.

ROBOPASS

TYPE: ROCK-STEEL
ABILITY: STURDY-MAGNET PULL
HEIGHT: 1.4m
WEIGHT: 340.0kg

Probopass exudes strong magnetism from all over its hard body. The Rock-Steel type controls three small units that are commonly referred to as Mini-Noses.

PURUGLY

TYPE: NORMAL
ABILITY: THICK FAT-OWN TEMPO
HEIGHT: 1.0m
WEIGHT: 43.8kg

Evolved from Glameow, this cat-like Pokémon is a force to be reckoned with. Purugly has a reputation for barging its way into the nests of others and claiming the contents as its own.

RAICHU

TYPE: ELECTRIC
ABILITY: STATIC
HEIGHT: 0.8m
WEIGHT: 30.0kg

Much heavier than Pikachu, Raichu turns aggressive if it does not expend the electrical energy it has stored in its body. The stores of voltage are released through its tail.

ROTOM

TYPE: ELECTRIC-GHOST
ABILITY: LEVITATE
HEIGHT: 0.3m
WEIGHT: 0.3kg

Rotom's body is composed of plasma. This Pokémon has no evolutions. Although it is small, Rotom's ability to infiltrate electronic gadgets gives it the power to cause chaos.

SHELLOS

EAST ←SEA

WEST SEA→

TYPE: WATER
ABILITY: STICKY HOLD-STORM DRAIN
HEIGHT: 0.3m
WEIGHT: 6.3kg

Shellos' colour and shape vary from region to region, but Sinnoh versions are either pink or blue with yellow markings. It evolves into the soft-bodied Gastrodon.

That afternoon the students lined up for the first part of the Triathlon – the Pokémon ride. Dawn gave Piplup a well-earned rest, putting him back in her Poké Ball. Angie did the same with Shinx.
"On your marks, get set," shouted Professor Rowan.
"Hang on tight buddy," Ash told Pokémon, just as the Professor called "Go!"
The students thundered away towards the first collection point, where they were due to pick up a Poké Ball and find out which Pokémon they'd be riding. To everyone's surprise, Jessilinda streaked into the lead.
"Make way for the fastest feet in foot racing!" she called, sprinting towards the collection point.
"Now, my reward!" she smirked as she picked her Poké Ball and summoned forth her Pokémon.

To Jessie's horror a Hippowdon appeared before her.
"Sorry, bad choice!" she yelled. She told the Pokémon to take a hike then attempted to steal another Poké Ball. Luckily however, the assistant manning the station spotted her and blew his whistle. "The exchanging of Poké Balls is forbidden," he growled, sending Jessie sulking back to Hippowdon. Jessie had wasted so much time that the rest of the field had now caught up. Ash, Dawn, Brock and

Angie arrived and one after the other commanded their Pokémon out of their chosen ball.
Ash got a Spoink. Dawn a Dodrio.
"Great! Onix looks strong," Brock cried in delight, seeing the stone-like snake appear.
"So does my Ariados," said Angie, jumping on its back and speeding off.
Soon they were way ahead. Ordering Hippowdon to catch up, a reluctant Jessie mounted it and tried desperately to hold on as it used its Sand Tomb move to burrow through the earth.

From their hot air balloon, the teaching assistants surveyed the course and gave a running commentary, sending live footage back to Professor Rowan's laptop. Rowan and Nurse Joy sat glued to the screen. "With that kind of enthusiasm, the outcome is anyone's guess!" said the Professor, watching the students' progress. "I just hope no one ends up getting hurt!"

said an always-caring Joy. "Right Chansey?" She was right to be concerned – out front things were getting dangerous. Ash, Dawn, Brock and Angie spurred their Pokémon on to greater speeds and jostled for first position. "C'mon Spoink, we can't lose!" shouted Ash. "Pedal to the metal Onix," said Brock. Angie and Ariados scuttled into the lead as the group approached the lake.

Further back the rest of the students were doing their best, although some were really struggling to master their Pokémon. "Outta the way!" screamed one of Jessie's Green Team boys as his Garchomp came hurtling past. Other students pulled up their Pokémon, but one girl riding Drapion was too late. They all came crashing down in a huge multi-people and Pokémon pile-up. Only one person remained unaffected by the crash – Conway. "I had a feeling digging some holes and travelling underground was the only way to go!" he laughed, surveying the blocked road.

Once in the courtyard the atmosphere became tense. Ash's attitude had irritated Angie. "For your information Ash," she blurted out. "The Triathlon is a lot more intense than you think!" "Go ahead and say what you want, I'm gonna get first place!" he replied angrily. "No that'll be me," Angie fired back. "You're better off aiming for second." In the end it took Dawn to break up the fight.

"Relax you two!" said Brock. "No matter which one of you finishes first, it's the same points if the other comes in second!" "May the best guy win then," retorted Ash. Angie was about to come back with another insult, but a sudden flashback of Ash hanging on to her hand stopping her being sucked into the Spirit World made her think again. Ash might be her rival, but he had saved her life.

Dawn meanwhile had her own rival to deal with. Out of nowhere Conway appeared behind her. He'd helped her out in the past, but now he seemed rather odd. "Well Dawn, it's almost that time," he said creepily. "I've been spending a hours analyzing every last bit of data I've collected on you throughout the week. I've now come to the conclusion you're going to be my most formidable rival in the Pokémon Triathlon." Dawn was dumbfounded. "Your rival?" she asked. "That's right," hissed Conway. "I've got you marked, see!" His face was inches from hers before he slunk away. "What's up with that guy?" Dawn wondered.

Professor Rowan greeted nurse Joy and Chansey, who would be on hand during the event in case any of the students got injured. Brock did his usual swooning when he saw Joy's pretty face, but a painful prod from Croagunk's toxic fingers snapped him out of his stupor. On a sunbed nearby, Team Rocket's Jessie, was still masquerading as Jessilinda. Ever more popular with the younger students, she was now being fanned by some of her most ardent fans. "No-one wants to get a sunburn at my age," she laughed as the cool air lapped her body. "I've got to save my seventeen-ish silky skin. "Good luck Ms Jessilinda," said one boy. "You'll be great!" "The Green Team probably isn't gonna win, but we'll fight 'til the bitter end," added another one.

These words were enough to bring Jessie to her feet, prompting the kind of rant she usually saved for her Team Rocket chums. "Excuse me but the Green Team never gives up!" she bellowed. "Faith and hope spring eternal! All for one and one to win!" Her team burst into applause. James and Meowth watched the display, still disguised as maintenance staff. "Jessie's team spirit is on full burn!" said James. "Her empty head can't seem to grasp that the Green Team's winning chances are zip, zero, nada," muttered Meowth. "It would be good for our future health if Jessie were to take that victory lap," dreamed James. "Of course!" nodded Meowth. "And we could help out by getting sneaky." "I just love a good sneak!" James chuckled.

SHINX

TYPE: ELECTRIC

ABILITY: RIVALRY-INTIMIDATE

HEIGHT: 0.5m

WEIGHT: 9.5kg

This bright-eyed blue Pokémon can blind its enemies with its dazzling electrically-charged coat. Whenever it senses danger, its fur starts to crackle and light up. Shinx evolves into Luxio then Luxray.

SKUNTANK

TYPE: POISON-DARK

ABILITY: STENCH-AFTERMATH

HEIGHT: 1.0m

WEIGHT: 38.kg

Skuntank can spray its prey with a vile-smelling liquid from distances of up to 50 metres. The toxic drops are ejected from the tip of its tail. The Poison-Dark type evolves from Stunky.

SNOVER

TYPE: ICE-GRASS

ABILITY: SNOW WARNING

HEIGHT: 1.0m

WEIGHT: 50.5kg

Snover dwells in high mountain ranges. Despite infrequent contact with humans, the Pokémon is curious enough to approach visitors. Its long arms are very expressive.

SPIRITOMB

TYPE: GHOST-DARK

ABILITY: PRESSURE

HEIGHT: 1.0m

WEIGHT: 108kg

This strange-looking Pokémon does not evolve. Instead, Spiritomb is a blend of 108 spirits. It is attached to a crack in a mysterious keystone.

STUNKY

TYPE: POISON-DARK

ABILITY: STENCH-AFTERMATH

HEIGHT: 0.4m

WEIGHT: 19.2kg

Like Skuntank, Stunky protects itself by spraying an evil-smelling liquid from its rear. The stench lingers for at least 24 hours and is so pungent it can induce vomiting.

YANMEGA

TYPE: BUG-FLYING

ABILITY: SPEED BOOST-TINTED LENS

HEIGHT: 1.9m

WEIGHT: 51.5kg

Yanma's more powerful evolution can move its wings at an awesome rate. Its power is such that it can create shock waves with sufficient force to cause internal injuries to its prey.

ONE TEAM, TWO TEAM, RED TEAM, BLUE TEAM!

As the end of the Pokémon Summer Academy looms, the trainers and Pokémon eagerly await Professor Rowan's last announcement. What will the final event be?

Brock, Dawn, Ash and Angiecould hardly contain their excitement. Professor Rowan had just announced that the final activity at the Summer Academy would be the Pokémon Triathlon. Everyone stared at the diagram on the blackboard which showed the course. "The starting line is here at the Academy, and everyone will begin simultaneously," explained the teaching assistant.

"We have prepared a Poké Ball for each of you, but you'll have no idea which Pokémon it contains."
"So we work with whatever Pokémon pops out!" whispered Dawn.
The course would take them through the forest and lake. They'd be using a Water-type to cross the lake and after that they'd run a marathon to bring them back to the finish.

The instructor drummed in a couple more rules before dismissing the class.
"Under no circumstances should you attack or battle with any other teams," he said. "First place earns fifty points, second earns thirty points, third place, twenty points and all our remaining participants will receive ten points apiece."
There was good news for the Red Team – which included Ash, Dawn, Brock and Angie. The overall points total was to be calculated using the points earned by all the Red Team players, meaning that if they did well, they'd still be able to overtake the Blues.
"Great," said Ash, getting fired up.
"We're going to show them. Those fifty points are going to be all mine!"

HAVE YOU GOT THE NERVE TO BRING THESE GHOST-TYPE POKÉMON TO LIFE? USE YOUR MOST EERIE SHADES TO COLOUR THEM IN, THEN WRITE THEIR NAMES BELOW. USE THE INFORMATION IN THIS ANNUAL TO IDENTIFY THEM.

CAMP QUIZ

PART 2

QUESTION 3

CRANIDOS, GEODUDE AND ONIX ALL BELONG TO WHICH POKÉMON TYPE?

A. GROUND ☐

B. STEEL ☐

C. ROCK ☐

QUESTION 2

WHERE DOES GIRATINA USUALLY DWELL?

A. THE REVERSE WORLD ☐

B. THE SPIRIT WORLD ☐

C. ON THE DEEP SEA FLOOR ☐

QUESTION 4

DAWN'S GOAL IN LIFE IS TO BECOME A TOP POKÉMON...

A. CO-ORDINATOR ☐

B. TRAINER ☐

C. MASTER ☐

QUESTION 1

WHAT TYPE OF POKÉMON IS CHERRIM?

A. BUG ☐

B. GRASS ☐

C. GROUND ☐

QUESTION 5

PROBOPASS CAN BRING THINGS TOWARDS IT WITH ITS...

A. MAGNETIC FORCE ☐

B. GLOWING LIGHT ☐

C. HYPNOTIC MOVEMENTS ☐

Reaching the water's edge first, Angie thanked Ariados for its speed and picked up her next Poké Ball. Immediately a blue, crested Lapras appeared so she hopped on and took to the water. Just behind her came Ash, Dawn and Brock who thanked their Pokémon and grabbed another ball. Speeding through the water Angie was feeling confident.

"Grabbing first place will be a piece of cake," she said to herself.

But Ash wasn't done trying. Within minutes he'd caught up on the back of his Mantyke. "Comin' through!" he called, tearing past Angie. "Like that's going to happen!" she yelled. She urged Lapras to use Ice Beam, sending them shooting ahead. "See ya later!" she called to Ash.

"Those two sure know how to mix it up don't they?" said Brock, as he and Dawn sped along side-by-side. "Well six can play at that game!" Dawn shrieked. "Quick Sharpedo, let's move!" The huge shark-like Pokémon prepared to lurch forward, but suddenly a wave broke in front of them and a boy emerged riding a Floatzel. "It's Conway!" cried Dawn. "Guilty as charged!" replied Conway. "I'll catch up with you later!" He disappeared below the surface once more.

Soon all the students had begun part two of the competition and were heading across the lake. All but one, that is. Jessie's Hippowdon eventually lumbered up to the Poké Ball station.
"I have had it!" she screamed, forgetting she was in disguise. "I don't recall this being in my job description."
Suddenly noticing the assistant staring at her in confusion, she politely thanked Hippowdon and put it back in its ball.
"Jessie's dead last and sinking fast!" sighed James, looking on from behind a tree.
"Maybe we should give that girl's Pokémon a little submariney-type boost!" added Meowth. There was no time to act however. Jessie hurled her Poké Ball into the water, only

to find it contained a Magikarp.
"I need you like I need too much sun!" she yelped, shaking it by the fin.
In response Magikarp dragged her under the water then jumped high into the sky, landing Jessie with a dunking.

"Since when does a Magikarp move like that?" wondered James, watching the pair zip into the distance.
Meowth was equally amazed. "That Professor sure knows how to pick Pokémon with primo pizzazzed pluck!"
Meanwhile Ash and Angie were neck and neck at the far shore. They thanked their Water-types and Angie called out Shinx for

the final marathon part of the Triathlon. Without another word to Angie and Shinx, Ash and Pikachu sprinted away.
"There's been a change!" The commentator's voice boomed down from the hot air balloon. "Jessilinda from the Green Team has suddenly and dramatically jumped from last to third place." Sure enough a drenched Jessie emerged from the water after a rollercoaster ride with Magikarp.

Laughing madly, Jessie was in no mood to be modest. "Finally you can feast your eyes on what I'm really made of!"

"I must say an impressive feat…" came a voice behind her. Jessie whipped round to discover Conway.

"Perhaps it might have been a smarter choice for me to keep tabs on you rather than on Dawn," he chuckled creepily.

Angie and Ash were still in the lead. "I'm not losing to the likes of you Ash Ketchum and that's final" puffed Angie, looking over her shoulder to see whether Ash had fallen behind. "You're gonna be changing your mind real soon!" Ash panted. Behind them, a screaming Jessie was gaining ground, accompanied by Seviper. Jessie's feet were spurred on by the fact that Conway appeared to be stalking her. "Go pick on someone from your own planet!" she yelled. Conway wasn't fazed. "Once I start keeping tabs on someone I don't stop!" he laughed.

With her usual Team Rocket hastiness and lack of forethought, Jessie had underestimated the boy's speed. Conway deftly dodged Seviper's blow, leaving the Pokémon to crack its skull on the rock face and slide to the floor. "I guess that settles that!" smiled Conway, sprinting out of the cave's exit. I've won it along with my Blue Team! I guess my tab-keeping time on you is over." A humiliated Jessie could only scream her reply. "Nooooooo!"
Conway had soundly beaten her – she just couldn't believe it.

Angie couldn't believe her bad luck either. Usually she managed to avoid sticky situations, but since being at Summer Camp she'd already risked her life on several occasions. Now she found herself trying to stop herself and Shinx from plummeting to infinity by using just her feet. "I'll get us outta here Shinx," she told the shaking Pokémon, trying to steady her voice.

Thinking back, Angie remembered the last time she'd been in real danger. The day before she'd almost been sucked off to who knows where, but Ash had saved her. She looked up, imagining she was seeing his face again. But wait, it was Ash and he was leaning his hand down to catch hers! "Hold on tight!" he called. The brave Trainer gripped Angie's wrist and began to pull. "Thanks," she gasped.

On the surface, first Conway and then Jessie burst out of the cave and into the open. There were intakes of breath from the commentator as he reported this news through his microphone to Professor Rowan and the other spectators.

"C'mon Angie, just a little more!" yelled Ash, hauling Angie and Shinx up the last few metres to safety. The pair landed panting in a heap. "Hey you two," asked Ash. "You hangin' in there?" "We're fine!" responded Angie. The rivals sat in friendly silence for a few minutes until they'd all got their breath back. Then, sitting up, Ash's competitive spirit returned. "It's not over yet!" he yelled. "Let's turn this thing around!" "I'm not going easy on you just cause you saved me!" said Angie. "Didn't think you would," grinned Ash

Back at the school, the teachers waited in a state of high anticipation at the finish line for the first students to return. Who would win? Finally they got their answer. "It's Conway, followed by Jessilinda!" cried the commentator as the pair appeared at the gates. What a sorry sight they were. Bent over double they could barely put one foot in front of the other. Even their Pokémon were exhausted. "Not doing a little cardio training was pretty dumb," groaned Conway. Jessie, who was almost asleep, still managed to bully her Pokémon. "Put some spring into your step Seviper!" James was concerned. "Jessie looks like she just got back from shopping."

"With a bounced credit card!" added Meowth. "With all that living it up in the lap of luxury she's gotten a little soft around the middle."

As Conway and Jessie continued to plod round the courtyard there was a ripple of excitement among the teachers. "Look at that! Here come both Ash and Angie!" roared the commentator. "The outcome of this race is still up for grabs!" Conway and Jessie tried to make out what was happening.

The next few seconds unfolded in slow motion. Ash and Angie raced through the gates towards the finish line, determination etched on their faces. Conway and Jessie spun round, and then dragged their heavy limbs towards the end. The commentator jumped up and down in excitement – never before had he witnessed a Triathlon like this.

"Hang in there Jessie… I mean Jessilinda!" called James from the sidelines. It was too late, Ash dipped his head and snapped the finish tape, with Angie just a step behind. It was all over. The Red Team had taken first and second place. Jessie and Conway collapsed in a heap on the line, their dreams shattered. "Congratulations Ash!" said Angie as the talented Trainer punched the air to the rapturous applause of the rest of the team.

"My Pokémon expertise was unassailable, but my endurance was strictly sub par," said Conway. "Next time I grace the hallowed halls of the Summer Academy I'm majoring in food service!" said an exhausted Jessie.

Professor Rowan stepped up to announce the results. "Congratulations to the Red Team on their victory!" Nurse joy offered her congratulations to the Blue and Green competitors, before adding that she was especially pleased no-one had got hurt. "And so I say goodbye with my one wish for all of you," said the emotional Professor. "I hope that the friendship you have with all Pokémon deepens, and that you always learn from each other." The students each admired their winners' plaques. "I'm gonna remember this forever!" said Brock.

That night it was finally time to relax! The students enjoyed a huge bonfire in the courtyard. The sky was full of stars and everyone sat around eating, drinking and chatting about what they would do now the camp was over. One person, lurking on the fringes of the party seemed particularly sad.

"I feel empty knowing it's all finished," James said wistfully. Meowth however, could only think about his empty tummy.

"I have the sneaking suspicion that we've forgotten something," said James.

"Like the whole point of being here?" added Meowth.

The two thought a moment, and then gave up. Instead they decided to concentrate on the fact that they'd been paid for their time and for once they'd had comfortable board and lodgings.

Jessie meanwhile was tucking into the food after all her efforts. Summer Camp had even had a positive effect on her – she seemed visibly moved when her team members approached and gave a heartfelt speech about their awesome week with Ms Jessilinda.

"Aren't you nice?" she smiled at her fans. "Clueless… but thank you!"

Ash spotted Angie sitting on a log, gazing at the sky. "What's wrong?" he asked. "It's the last night," she said quietly. 'I must have gone to the Pokémon Summer Academy a million times before, but this year was hands down the best one yet!" Ash admitted he'd had fun too. "You know the most amazing thing was that you saved my life twice!" Angie smiled. "You and I… we're friends!" nodded Ash. Angie smiled.

Sadly all good things come to an end. At last the bonfire died and the students began drifting off to bed.

"We'll meet again no doubt," said Ash as the friends parted ways the next day. "I'll come and see you the next time I get to Solaceon Town," he added. "We'll battle!" "That'll be nice," Angie beamed. "I can't wait!"

An experience like the Summer Academy doesn't come along every day, but ourHeroes took full advantage of the opportunity. With Celestic Town next on their itinerary, the gang's exciting Sinnoh journey continues...

CAMP QUIZ

PART 3

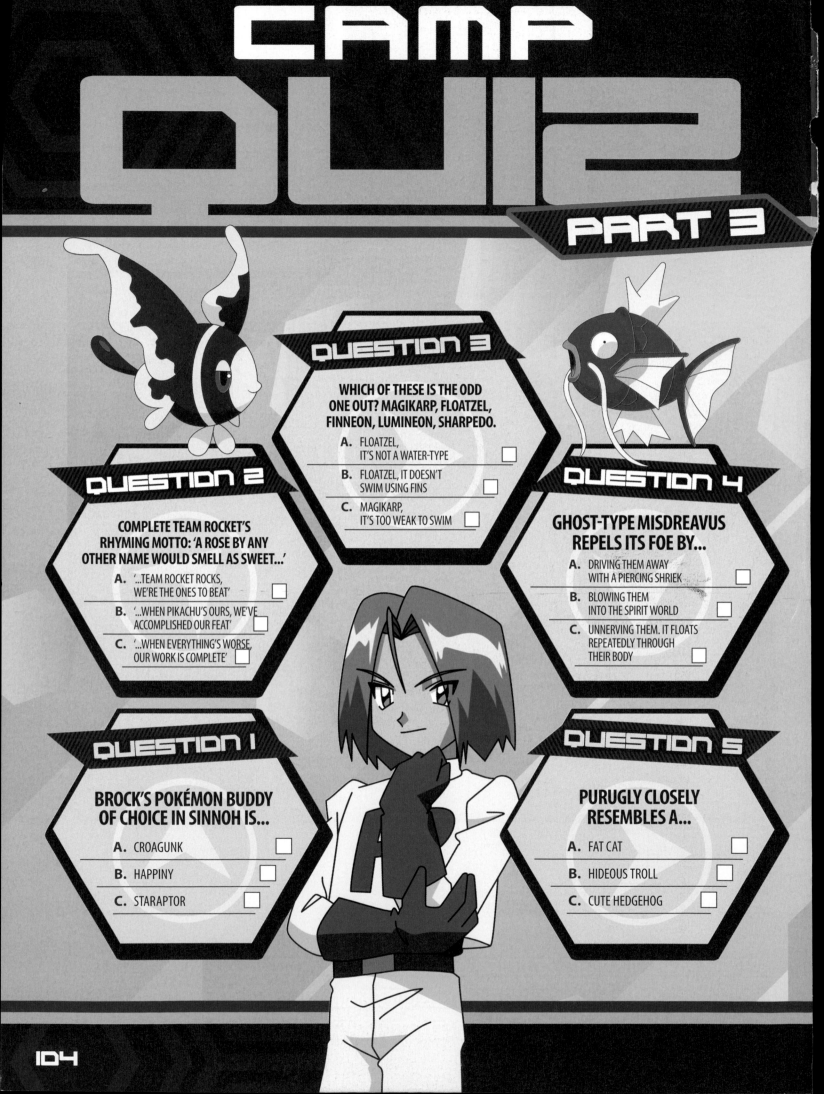

QUESTION 3

WHICH OF THESE IS THE ODD ONE OUT? MAGIKARP, FLOATZEL, FINNEON, LUMINEON, SHARPEDO.

A. FLOATZEL, IT'S NOT A WATER-TYPE ☐

B. FLOATZEL, IT DOESN'T SWIM USING FINS ☐

C. MAGIKARP, IT'S TOO WEAK TO SWIM ☐

QUESTION 2

COMPLETE TEAM ROCKET'S RHYMING MOTTO: 'A ROSE BY ANY OTHER NAME WOULD SMELL AS SWEET...'

A. '...TEAM ROCKET ROCKS, WE'RE THE ONES TO BEAT' ☐

B. '...WHEN PIKACHU'S OURS, WE'VE ACCOMPLISHED OUR FEAT' ☐

C. '...WHEN EVERYTHING'S WORSE, OUR WORK IS COMPLETE' ☐

QUESTION 4

GHOST-TYPE MISDREAVUS REPELS ITS FOE BY...

A. DRIVING THEM AWAY WITH A PIERCING SHRIEK ☐

B. BLOWING THEM INTO THE SPIRIT WORLD ☐

C. UNNERVING THEM. IT FLOATS REPEATEDLY THROUGH THEIR BODY ☐

QUESTION 1

BROCK'S POKÉMON BUDDY OF CHOICE IN SINNOH IS...

A. CROAGUNK ☐

B. HAPPINY ☐

C. STARAPTOR ☐

QUESTION 5

PURUGLY CLOSELY RESEMBLES A...

A. FAT CAT ☐

B. HIDEOUS TROLL ☐

C. CUTE HEDGEHOG ☐

OK, you're on the home stretch. Question is, are you an A Grade student? You may have made a few mistakes so far but head down and concentrate. As Ash would say, it's time to turn this thing around!

QUESTION 6

ANGIE'S POKÉMON TRAVELLING COMPANION IN SINNOH IS...

A. SEALEO

B. SHINX

C. ARIADOS

QUESTION 8

WHICH HUGE GROUND POKÉMON BLASTS SAND THROUGH HOLES IN ITS BODY?

A. HIPPOWDON

B. GABITE

C. TORTERRA

QUESTION 10

GLACEON IS ONE OF HOW MANY PARALLEL EVOLUTIONS OF EEVEE?

A. SEVEN

B. THREE

C. FIVE

QUESTION 7

WHICH OF THE FOLLOWING IS NOT A MOVE TYPICALLY USED BY YANMEGA?

A. SONIC BOOM

B. STEEL WING

C. WATER PULSE

YOUR SCORE

___ / 30

QUESTION 9

WHICH OF THESE POKÉMON IS THE HEAVIEST?

A. HIPPOPOTAS

B. BRONZONG

C. DUSKNOIR

NOW TOTAL UP YOUR SCORES FROM ALL THREE TESTS TO SEE IF YOU'VE PASSED THE ENTRANCE EXAMINATION.

0–10: Good try! But you're not quite ready to take on the gruelling Camp challenges just yet. You'll need to re-sit. Why not read through the correct answers and memorise them, then test and score a friend. All that revising will stand you in good stead for your next attempt.

10–20: Well done! You're shaping up to be just the kind of student Professor Rowan wants on his courses. However, as this year's Camp is full, he suggests you defer your place until next summer and in the meantime swat up on the subjects which foxed you this time round.

20–30: Congratulations Clever Clogs! You've passed with flying colours and are in! Better get packing now for the gruelling journey up Mount Coronet. The Professor's inventory includes warm clothes for the Ghostly night hunts, waterproofs for the lake tasks and your best running shoes for the Triathlon. Have fun!

POKÉMON
PHOTO LINE
MAKE IT!

ASH, BROCK AND DAWN KNOW JUST HOW IMPORTANT FRIENDS ARE, THAT'S WHY THEY LOVE THIS MAKE-IT! MAKE THIS COOL POKÉMON PHOTO LINE AND YOU'LL BE ABLE TO SEE YOUR PALS EVERY DAY TOO.

YOU WILL NEED:

- Scissors
- White paper
- Felt tip pens or crayons
- 6 wooden clothes pegs
- Double-sided sticky tape or glue
- String or ribbon around 1.5-2 metres long
- Photos of your friends (or family)

1. Cut out the images of Ash, Brock, Dawn, Pikachu, Piplup and Croagunk on these pages using the dotted outline to guide you. If you'd rather, trace the pictures onto white paper and colour them in.

2. Fix one character onto the flat side of each clothes peg, using the glue or tape to hold them in place.

3. Now put your length of string up horizontally between two points, just like a washing line.

4. Use your cool Pokémon character clips to hang photos of your pals along the string, and then enjoy! Now you'll never be without your pals, even when you're on your own!

Scissors can be dangerous. Ask an adult to help you when cutting out the character shapes. Check with them first before hanging up the ribbon or string.

PAGE 13: EVOLVED AND IMPROVED

GARCHOMP HAS

1. A yellow patch on its abdomen
2. A yellow marking on its head
3. Two extra spikes on its wings
4. A longer tail
5. Two spikes of equal size and shape on its thighs, rather than having one bigger than the other like Gabite
6. Crests at each side of head set further apart
7. No light grey markings that Gabite has on each crest
8. Three circle-like markings around each ankle plus...
9. Garchomp is taller than Gabite
10. Gabite is the heavier Pokémon

PAGE 30: DOUBLE VISION

There are 14 Raichus

PAGES 32: CAMP QUIZ PART 1

1-C 2-A 3-B 4-A 5-C 6-A 7-A 8-B 9-C 10-B

PAGE 34 – GRASS-TYPE WORD GRID

G	L	I	S	E	P	W	O	M	B
W	E	N	S	C	L	E	A	I	L
O	A	X	E	G	M	D	E	R	E
N	F	T	F	Z	A	U	R	R	A
S	O	A	I	M	R	B	U	E	F
A	N	B	R	U	Q	U	T	H	E
M	U	O	C	F	V	E	N	C	O
O	W	M	V	O	L	P	D	I	N
B	D	R	E	E	L	T	O	R	G
A	R	F	T	U	R	T	W	I	G

PAGE 35: THE ROUTE TO ROWAN

PAGES 38: WHO GOES WHERE?

1. **Chansey** – Hospitals
2. **Shaymin** – Flowery Meadows
3. **Onix** – Underground
4. **Snover** – Mountains
5. **Lumineon** – Ocean floor
6. **Golduck** – Lakes
7. **Grotle** – Forest
8. **Bibarel** – Dams
9. **Geodude** – Mountain trails
10. **Gible** – Caves

PAGE 57: EVOLUTION SOLUTIONS

1. DRIFBLIM
2. YANMEGA
3. STUNKY / SKUNTANK
4. PORYGON-Z
5. SHINX / LUXIO
6. GABITE / GARCHOMP

IDB

PAGES 58: CODED CORRESPONDENCE

Hi Angie,
How is it going? I hope both you and Shinx are well? Are things busy at the Pokémon Day Care centre? Dawn, Brock and I are really missing you. We can't believe we'll have to wait a whole year before the next Camp. We're off to our next gym, but I'll try to come visit you real soon. Love. Ash

Hi Ash,
Thanks for your letter. Sorry it's taken me so long to reply, things have been really hectic here at work and I've been trying to train Shinx to pull some new moves. I miss you all too and can't wait to go back to Mount Coronet next year. Your friend and rival, Angie

PAGE 60: MEDITITE'S MIND-READING

How to do the trick:

- Hand the different coloured crayons to the spectator.

- Turn around and extend your hands behind your back, then ask your friend to give you a crayon.

- Turn around to face them.

- With your hands still behind your back, subtly mark your thumbnail with the crayon. Say that you're trying to 'visualize' what colour it might be.

- Hand the crayon back.

- Pretend to concentrate and then bring your hand (with the crayon mark on the thumbnail) up to rest on your forehead (as if you're thinking). Make sure this gesture looks natural. Sneak a peek at your thumb.

- Put your hand down but continue to pretend to think then reveal the correct colour!

PAGE 61 – SWEET SHADOWS

A. PACHIRISU
B. BUNEARY
C. TURTWIG
D. SHAYMIN (LAND FORME)
E. PIPLUP
F. CHIMCHAR
G. PIKACHU

PAGE 64: WATER COMES NEXT?

1)   2)   3)   4)

PAGE 65 – CAMP CROSSWORD

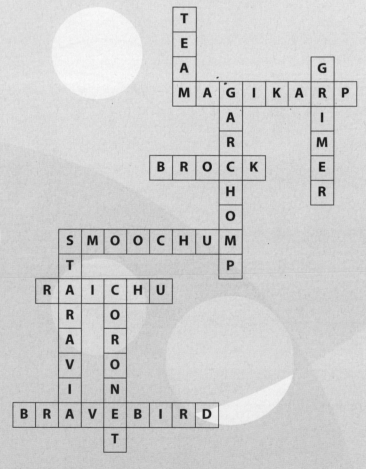

PAGES 82: CREEPY COLOUR-IN

Duskull and Misdreavus

PAGES 84: CAMP QUIZ – PART 2

1-B   2-A   3-C   4-A   5-A   6-A   7-B   8-C   9-A   10-B

PAGES 104: CAMP QUIZ – PART 3

1-A   2-C   3-B   4-A   5-A   6-B   7-C   8-A   9-B   10-A